M000032535

TRIGONOMETRY SELF-TAUGHT

BY PETER H. SELBY

Senior Research Engineer
General Dynamics/Astronautics

Formerly Flight Training Supervisor
Convair Division, San Diego

McGraw-Hill Book Company, New York • Toronto • London

Affectionately Dedicated
to DOROTHY SCOTT HOOPER
for much patient guidance

TRIGONOMETRY SELF–TAUGHT

Copyright © 1964 by McGraw-Hill, Inc.

All rights reserved, including the right to reproduce this book,
or any portion thereof, in any form, without permission by the
Publisher.

Printed in the United States of America
Library of Congress Catalog Card Number 64–16493

111213141516171   MUMU   8987654321
ISBN 07-056069-2

PREFACE

You will find the material in this book presented in a different way than you are accustomed to in an ordinary textbook. The first thing you will notice is that you are given only a small amount of information at a time, then immediately asked an appropriate question to help you find out how much you have understood, just as an individual tutor would do. The answer you select in each case determines the item of information you will be given next; hence your route through the course. This is a special kind of self-teaching technique known as "programmed instruction" or "auto-instruction."

Your rate of progress—the time you spend and the amount of material you read—is, therefore, up to you. You can go as rapidly or as slowly as your aptitude and inclination permit.

If this is the first time you have studied a subject presented in this new way, you should find it an interesting way to learn.

Whom This Course Is For

This book is intended primarily for the following two groups:

1. Those individuals who want or need to know something about the principles and techniques involved in solving mathematical problems which require, or can be simplified by the use of, trigonometry, and who are being exposed to this subject for the first time.

2. Those who may have learned something about trigonometry in high school or college (perhaps a long while ago), but who have had little occasion to use their knowledge since and now require a brief review of the subject in order to apply it to their work or to further study.

CONTENTS

What You Can Expect to Learn from This Course

This specialized course of instruction is by no means all-inclusive. It is intended only to familiarize you with the basic concepts underlying the use of trigonometry and to assist you in learning how to apply these concepts in solving problems.

Specifically, at the conclusion of this course, you should be generally familiar with the theory and practical techniques of solving plane right triangles with the aid of a table of natural trigonometric functions. You should also be able to demonstrate your knowledge by scoring at least 45 on the self-administered quiz found at the back of this book.

It is assumed that the reader has had a first course in algebra and geometry at some point in his educational career. However, lack of this background will *not* necessarily bar you from successful completion of this program, since the author has endeavored to explain all needed terms and concepts. (Be sure to look in the Glossary for an explanation of words or expressions that are not familiar to you.)

If a general familiarity with trigonometry is as much as you want (or need), practicing what this program will teach you should in time make you skillful in solving problems involving plane triangles through the use of the natural trigonometric functions.

However, if you wish to learn how logarithms can be used to aid in the solution of problems in trigonometry, as well as to simplify complex problems in multiplication, division, raising numbers to higher powers, and extracting roots of numbers, you will find assistance in a companion volume titled "Logarithms Self-Taught."

Readers who desire or need a broader background in the field of trigonometry will find ample practice problems and detailed consideration of other theoretical and applied aspects of the subject in any good, standard classroom textbook. The author hopes that completion of the present program will at least have served to start you on a fascinating highway—one you can follow as far as you care to travel.

What the Reader Needs to Know about This Book

This is no ordinary book. Although the pages are numbered consecutively, they are not intended to be read consecutively.

At the bottom of each page, you will be told which page to turn to next. Follow these instructions and you will have no trouble staying on the intended path. This will aid us in presenting just the information you need to help you understand the subject matter.

To begin, start on page 1.

Trigonometry deals with triangles. A triangle is a geometric figure bounded by three lines. *Plane* trigonometry (which is the only kind of trigonometry we will be concerned with in this book) deals with *plane* triangles, that is, triangles formed by the intersection of three *straight* lines (as distinguished from spherical triangles, which lie on the surface of a sphere and therefore are bounded by curved lines).

A *plane,* of course, is simply a flat (two-dimensional) surface.

Does any of this sound familiar to you? If you studied geometry in high school, you probably have been exposed to these terms and concepts before. If you didn't, it won't really make any difference, since we'll explain them as we go along.

Let's see how well you're getting along so far.

Choose the statement below you consider correct, and turn to the page indicated.

The term "plane," as used in mathematics, is an abbreviation for *airplane.* **PAGE 4**

A plane triangle is one whose sides are straight lines lying in the same plane (i.e., not curved). **PAGE 6**

The sides of plane triangles are straight lines lying in different planes. **PAGE 3**

What are you doing here?

Apparently, you haven't followed instructions. Nowhere in the book are you directed to this page.

If you will recall, we warned you that you must follow the directions at the bottom of each page in order to stay on the right path. The book will not make much sense to you if you attempt to read the pages consecutively.

Now please return to page 1 and try again.

Your answer: The sides of plane triangles are straight lines that lie in different planes.

No, you missed an important point. You are right about the sides of a plane triangle being straight lines but not about their lying in *different* planes. The fact is that they must lie in the *same* plane; otherwise their ends wouldn't meet to form a triangle.

If you doubt this, just trace with your finger three adjoining edges of a cube (or any regular solid), taking a new direction at each corner, and then see if you can discover some way of getting these three edges to form a triangle in space. (If you find a way to do it, let us know.)

In the meantime, return to page 1, and pick a better answer.

Your answer: The term "plane," as used in mathematics,
                is an abbreviation for *airplane*.

No, this isn't so, although there is often some confusion on this point.   In talking about an airplane, we frequently shorten the term to *'plane*, replacing *air* with an apostrophe, or just *plane*, omitting the apostrophe.

But in *mathematics* (where the term really originated), when we say *plane*, we are talking about a two-dimensional surface, not a flying machine.

Now return to page 1 and choose the correct answer.

Now the fact that certain relationships exist between the sides and angles of a right triangle can be shown readily by the following illustration.

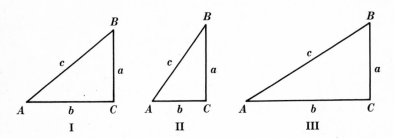

I   II   III

Note that the length of side a is the same in all three triangles. However, in example II, side b is shorter than in example I, and angle A is correspondingly larger. In example III, side b is larger than in example I, and angle A is correspondingly smaller.

It is apparent, therefore, that as the length of *side b increases* (side a remaining the same), the size of *angle A decreases*. Similarly, it can be shown that if *side a increases, b* remaining constant, *angle A increases;* the reverse also is true; i.e., if side a decreases, angle A decreases.

These are but a few of all the relationships existing between the sides and angles of a right triangle. They are sufficient, however, to show that *the size of an angle in a right triangle depends upon the ratio existing between any two sides of the triangle.*

Looking at the above triangles once more, what happens to the size of angle B as side b increases, side a remaining constant?

Angle B increases in size.   **PAGE 9**

Angle B decreases in size.   **PAGE 7**

Your answer: A plane triangle is one whose sides are
                straight lines lying in the same plane
                (i.e., not curved).

Correct!   I'm glad you caught this important point, because
therein lies the broad distinction between plane and spherical
triangles.   And if we're going to be talking about plane triangles,
we ought to know what they are as well as what they are *not*.
And they are *not* spherical triangles!

We stated previously that plane trigonometry deals with the
relationships existing between the sides and angles of triangles.
(Henceforth the term "triangle" will be used to designate a *plane*
triangle, unless otherwise indicated.)   More specifically, plane
trigonometry deals primarily with *right* triangles, that is, triangles
containing one right (90°) angle.

One of the triangles shown below is a right triangle.   See if
you can pick it out; then make a mental note of the Roman nu-
meral beneath it.

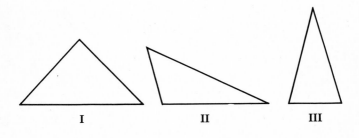

Now turn to page 8 to see if you picked the right one.

Your answer: Angle *B* decreases in size.

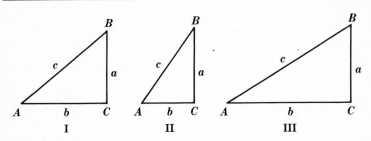

No, I think not.   Take another look at the three triangles (re-peated above for reference).   Don't they show precisely what happens to angle *B* as the length of side *b* changes?

Let's take example I as a standard.   Note that in example II the length of side *b* is *less* than in example I, and the size of angle *B* is correspondingly *smaller*.   Again, in example III, the length of side *b* is increased over what it was in example I, and the size of angle *B* is proportionately *greater*.

It is apparent, therefore, that (the length of side *a* remaining constant) the size of angle *B* will vary directly with the length of side *b;* thus if side *b* increases, angle *B* will increase accordingly.

Return to page 5 and select the right answer.

Correct answer: I

Did you get it right?   You should have—by the process of
elimination, if nothing else.   And you don't need a protractor to
do it!   Take another look.

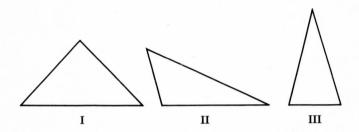

I   II   III

The angles in triangle III obviously are all less than 90°.
And of those in triangle II, one obviously is too large and the
others too small.   This leaves only triangle I, and although the
two angles at the base are evidently less than 90°, the one at
the top looks suspiciously like it *might* be a right angle.

If you turn the page so that one of the sides of this triangle
forms the base, it readily becomes apparent it *is* a right angle.

OK?   Then let's continue on page 5.

Your answer: Angle *B* increases in size.

Of course, you're quite correct.   The three triangles clearly show this, since in each triangle the length of side *b* differs, and the size of angle *B* varies correspondingly.

It's important that you have a clear concept of what we mean by the term "ratio," so let's consider it further for a moment.

The statement we made on page 5 was: The size of an angle in a right triangle depends upon the ratio existing between any two sides of the triangle.   A ratio is, of course, just one number divided by another.   We can either simply *indicate* the intended division by use of a fraction bar $\left(\frac{1}{9},\text{ for instance}\right)$ or we can *perform* the division, in which case the resulting number is said to be a "decimal fraction" or simply a "decimal" (0.1111, for example, carried to as many decimal places, or significant figures, as the nature of the problem requires).

To make sure you have the right idea of what we mean by "ratio," pick out the phrase below that correctly completes the statement given.

The ratio of one number (length of one side, in our case) to another number (length of another side) is the result of dividing the first number by the second; this division:

Must be indicated by a fraction bar.   **PAGE 11**

Must be performed and shown as a decimal fraction.   **PAGE 10**

May either be shown by use of a fraction bar or performed and shown as a decimal.   **PAGE 13**

Your answer: Must be performed and shown as a decimal
fraction.

No, I'm afraid you assumed that performing the actual division to arrive at a decimal expression of the ratio was a necessary
final step in the process. It is not. You *are* correct in thinking
that we usually take this step of dividing, but it's not *necessary*.

The relationship between two numbers, which we refer to as
a ratio, need only be *indicated*, for many purposes, either by use
of a fraction bar or in some other way. (A colon can be used,
for example, to express the same idea.)

Here are some examples of *indicated* ratios:

$\dfrac{4}{3}$ (the ratio of 4 to 3)

4:3 (also the ratio of 4 to 3)

$\dfrac{2}{9}$ or 2:9 (the ratio of 2 to 9)

$\dfrac{x}{y}$ or x:y (the ratio of x to y)

$\dfrac{\sqrt{3}}{2}$ (the ratio of the square root of 3, to 2)

Now take another look at the answers on page 9 and see if
you can't choose the right one.

Your answer: **Must be indicated by a fraction bar.**

No.   If you will recall, we said the division could simply be *indicated* (and a fraction bar is one conventional way of showing this, although there are other ways), *or* it could be *performed,* in which case we usually would get a decimal fraction (or at least a whole number and a decimal fraction).

A ratio can be indicated either way.

Let's look at a few examples.

Ratio of $\frac{6}{3}$ = 2.0000 (a whole number in this case)

Ratio of $\frac{3}{6}$ = 0.5000 (a decimal only)

Ratio of $\frac{4.5}{3}$ = 1.5000 (whole number and decimal)

Ratio of $\frac{4}{3}$ = 1.3333 (whole number and decimal fraction which can be carried to as many decimal places as necessary to the problem)

Now return to page 9 and select the correct answer.

Your answer: The ratio will be $\frac{8}{4}$, or 2.00 and angle A

will have decreased.

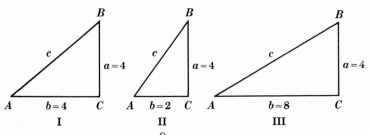

| I | II | III |

No, the ratio will not be $\frac{8}{4}$.   Either you have reversed the a and b values or you looked at example II instead of example III.   The ratio will be $\frac{4}{8}$, or 0.50.   However, the size of angle A will have *decreased;* you're quite right about that.   Thus we observe that, in this case at least, as the ratio between sides a and b grows smaller, angle A decreases in size.

Return to page 13 now, and choose the correct answer.

Your answer: May either be shown by use of a fraction
bar or performed and shown as a decimal.

You've got the point, all right. Of course, the use of a fraction bar isn't the **only** way to indicate a division [use of the division symbol ($\div$) is another way], but it's undoubtedly the most common.

Another point we should clear up is that our "decimal fraction" may at times be a whole number, although it seldom is in trigonometry. It also may be comprised of a whole number *and* a decimal fraction. We'll see some examples of this as we go along.

Now let's go back to our triangles again, consider some of the ratios we find there, and get a little practice in working them out.

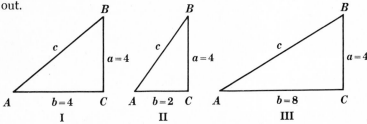

If, in the examples here, we let the sides have the numerical values indicated, then in example I the ratio of side a to side b $\left(\text{that is, } \dfrac{a}{b}\right)$ is $\dfrac{4}{4}$, or just 1 if we divide. What will be the ratio of a/b in example III, and what will happen to the size of angle A as compared with what it was in example I?

The ratio will be $\dfrac{4}{8}$, or 0.50, and angle A will have increased.   **PAGE 15**

The ratio will be $\dfrac{8}{4}$, or 2.00, and angle A will have decreased.   **PAGE 12**

The ratio will be $\dfrac{4}{8}$, or 0.50, and angle A will have decreased.   **PAGE 17**

Your answer: The sine of angle B would be b/a.

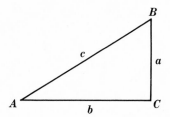

No, you're mistaken on this one. Remember that the sine of an angle is the ratio between the side opposite the angle and the *hypotenuse* of the right triangle. The side opposite angle B is b all right, but the hypotenuse is c, not a. The ratio of side b to side a is an important one in trigonometry, but it has another name and we'll talk about it later, not now.

So, return to page 16 and pick the right answer.

Your answer: The ratio will be $\frac{4}{8}$, or 0.50, and angle A
will have increased.

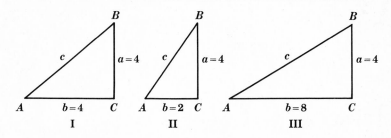

You're partly correct.   Look at example III again.   The ratio
of side *a* to side *b* (*a/b*) will certainly be $\frac{4}{8}$ or 0.50; that much is
right.   But will angle A have increased?   On the contrary, angle
A will have *decreased* in size.   This is a case where the size of
an angle decreases with a decrease in the value of the ratio between two sides.

Now return to page 13 and choose the right answer.

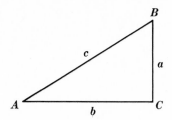

This matter of the relationships between the sides and angles of a right triangle is about all there is to plane trigonometry. And this statement is not intended in any sense to minimize those relationships, for they are all-important. They make possible the solution of a great many problems that otherwise would be very difficult to solve.

Because these relationships are so important, they have been carefully defined, and each has been given a name.

Thus, in the illustration, the ratio of the side opposite angle A to the side opposite the right angle is called the *sine of angle A.* Since the side opposite the right angle is called the "hypotenuse," the sine of angle A may be expressed as a ratio; thus

$$\text{sine } A = \frac{\text{opposite side}}{\text{hypotenuse}} \qquad \text{or} \qquad \sin A = \frac{a}{c}$$

The term "sine" usually is abbreviated, as shown, to "sin" but pronounced as though it still had the "e" on the end.

If the sine of an angle is the ratio of the side *opposite* an angle to the *hypotenuse* of a right triangle, what would be the sine of angle B?

The sine of angle B would be $\dfrac{b}{a}$ **PAGE 14**

The sine of angle B would be $\dfrac{b}{c}$ **PAGE 19**

The sine of angle B would be $\dfrac{c}{b}$ **PAGE 21**

Your answer: The ratio will be $\frac{4}{8}$, or 0.50, and angle A
will have decreased.

You're correct.   In this case, the size of angle A varies directly
with the value of the ratio between sides a and b; that is, as the
ratio becomes smaller, the size of angle A decreases and vice versa.

However, you must not fall into the error of thinking that the
size of an angle is always *directly* proportional to the ratio between two particular sides.   Consider what happens to the size of
angle B as the ratio between sides a and b changes.

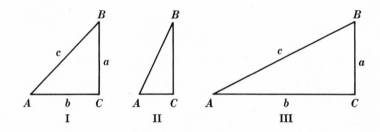

In example I, angle B appears approximately equal to angle
A.   But, in example III, where the ratio a/b has decreased by
50 per cent, angle B has increased in size.   We say, therefore,
that the size of angle B is *inversely* proportional to the ratio of
side a to side b.

Since the size of an angle depends on the ratio of the sides of
a triangle, it can be correctly inferred that, conversely, the length
of the sides will depend upon the size of the angle.   Thus, in the
triangles shown above, if angle A increases in size, side a will
increase; if angle B decreases in size, side b will decrease; etc.

Please see page 16 next.

Your answer: Five

No, you apparently forgot the *sine* ratio we discussed first. To produce all the relationships required to solve the various trigonometric problems that arise, we need to discover, state, and utilize all the possible combinations of the three sides of a right triangle, taken two at a time.

Take another look at the conventional right triangle shown at the top of page 19 and see how many combinations of two sides you can make; then select the correct answer at the bottom of that page.

Your answer: The sine of angle B would be b/c.

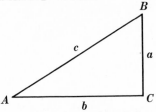

Very good. You weren't confused by the fact that we switched from angle *A* to angle *B*. Remember, in trigonometry, when we talk about variations in the size of an angle with changes in the lengths of the *sides* of a triangle, we have to talk about a *specific* angle and *two specific sides;* otherwise our discussion would be meaningless. Not only must we be sure which two sides we're referring to, but we've also got to be sure (since we're taking their ratio) that we have them in the right order $\left(\dfrac{2}{4} \text{ obviously is quite different from } \dfrac{4}{2}\right)$.

In addition to the sine, which we have been discussing, there are five additional relationships, or ratios, used in trigonometry. These relationships and their abbreviations are:

$$\text{cosine} \quad = \frac{\text{adjacent}}{\text{hypotenuse}} \quad \text{or} \quad \cos A = \frac{b}{c} \quad \text{or} \quad \cos B = \frac{a}{c}$$

$$\text{tangent} \quad = \frac{\text{opposite}}{\text{adjacent}} \quad \text{or} \quad \tan A = \frac{a}{b} \quad \text{or} \quad \tan B = \frac{b}{a}$$

$$\text{cosecant} \quad = \frac{\text{hypotenuse}}{\text{opposite}} \quad \text{or} \quad \csc A = \frac{c}{a} \quad \text{or} \quad \csc B = \frac{c}{b}$$

$$\text{secant} \quad = \frac{\text{hypotenuse}}{\text{adjacent}} \quad \text{or} \quad \sec A = \frac{c}{b} \quad \text{or} \quad \sec B = \frac{c}{a}$$

$$\text{cotangent} = \frac{\text{adjacent}}{\text{opposite}} \quad \text{or} \quad \cot A = \frac{b}{a} \quad \text{or} \quad \cot B = \frac{a}{b}$$

How many trigonometric ratios have we named so far?

Five   **PAGE 18**

Six   **PAGE 20**

Twelve   **PAGE 23**

Your answer: Six

Right!   There are only six possible combinations of the three sides of a right triangle, taken two at a time.   And I think you will find it comforting to know that these are all the relationships —together with their odd names—you are going to need to learn about in order to work problems in trigonometry.   Once you have *memorized* these ratios (and it is very important that you do so), the hardest part of the job is done.   Of course, you'll need practice in *using* them to solve problems, but it will be necessary to introduce very few additional concepts.

Now we would like you to recognize something about the six relationships we're discussing.   It is this: The last three equations (relationships) given you are merely reciprocals (upside down versions), of the first three!   Keep this in mind and you will find them easy to memorize.

Thus, to summarize,

$$\sin = \frac{\text{opposite}}{\text{hypotenuse}} \qquad \csc = \frac{\text{hypotenuse}}{\text{opposite}}$$

$$\cos = \frac{\text{adjacent}}{\text{hypotenuse}} \qquad \sec = \frac{\text{hypotenuse}}{\text{adjacent}}$$

$$\tan = \frac{\text{opposite}}{\text{adjacent}} \qquad \cot = \frac{\text{adjacent}}{\text{opposite}}$$

Just to make sure you remember what the abbreviations used above stand for, write in the full name of each of the trigonometric relationships in the spaces provided below.

sin ＿＿＿＿＿＿＿   csc ＿＿＿＿＿＿＿
cos ＿＿＿＿＿＿＿   sec ＿＿＿＿＿＿＿
tan ＿＿＿＿＿＿＿   cot ＿＿＿＿＿＿＿

To check your answers, turn to page 22.

Your answer: The sine of angle B would be c/b.

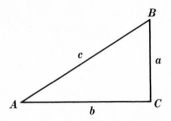

You picked the right sides, but you reversed their ratio.   The sine function represents the ratio of the side opposite an angle (side *b* in this case) to the hypotenuse of the triangle, not the other way around.   In other words, *b* over *c*, not *c* over *b*.   Got it?

Now pick the right answer on page 16, and we'll continue with our explanation of the various trigonometric ratios.

Correct answers:	sine	cosecant
	cosine	secant
	tangent	cotangent

If you had trouble with any of these terms, review them before going ahead; it is most important that they become old friends to you as quickly as possible.

Did you memorize the six trigonometric functions as you were asked? Let's see. Fill in the missing information below in terms of the sides of a right triangle (i.e., opposite, adjacent, and hypotenuse).

$\sin =$ ————————— $\csc =$ —————————

$\cos =$ ————————— $\sec =$ —————————

$\tan =$ ————————— $\cot =$ —————————

Check yourself by taking another look at page 20 (while still keeping your thumb on this page so you won't lose your place).

If you have them all right, you're ready to proceed to page 24. If you missed any, you'd better continue your study of these functions until you're sure you have them memorized before going on.

Your answer: Twelve

No. You've apparently included both the full and the abbreviated statements of each of the trigonometric ratios we gave
you.   The fuller expression given first in each case merely spells
out in words a relationship that is then restated more briefly in
letters.   But it's the *same* relationship in each case.

Now look again at the information on page 19 and then
select the correct answer.

Restating the functions in terms of angle A we get:

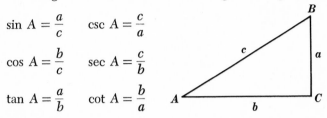

$$\sin A = \frac{a}{c} \qquad \csc A = \frac{c}{a}$$

$$\cos A = \frac{b}{c} \qquad \sec A = \frac{c}{b}$$

$$\tan A = \frac{a}{b} \qquad \cot A = \frac{b}{a}$$

Lest these terms and equations become too terrifying, it is well to bear in mind exactly what they signify. Let's take another look at the first equation. Putting it into prose it reads as follows: The sine of angle A is equal to the ratio of side a to side c; or, the sine of angle A is equal to the ratio of the *side opposite angle A* to the *hypotenuse* of the right triangle.

The terms sine, cosine, tangent, cosecant, secant, and cotangent are called "trigonometric functions," a term we will use quite commonly hereafter.

Actually the size of angle A (or angle B) is dependent upon the ratios existing between three sets of sides which, with their reciprocals, constitute six separate *trigonometric functions* as shown above; use of the term "sine," for instance, merely indicates *which* function we're talking about.

Use of a few examples will make this clear, so proceed to page 25, and we'll see if we can't give you some further help.

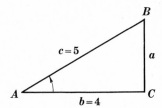

It's time we started giving some thought to how the different trigonometric functions can be used in a practical way to solve mathematical problems.

Referring to the familiar right-triangle figure shown, let us assume that the lengths of sides b and c are known and that it is desired to find the size of angle A.

$$b = 4 \qquad c = 5 \qquad A = ?$$

Our first step is to choose a trigonometric function involving the two known values and the unknown value under consideration. Here again are the choices open to us:

$$\sin A = \frac{a}{c} \qquad \csc A = \frac{c}{a}$$

$$\cos A = \frac{b}{c} \qquad \sec A = \frac{c}{b}$$

$$\tan A = \frac{a}{b} \qquad \cot A = \frac{b}{a}$$

Which one would you choose to aid you in the solution of this particular problem?

I would choose the sin function.   **PAGE 27**

I would choose the tan function.   **PAGE 29**

I would choose the cos function.   **PAGE 28**

Your answer: The reciprocal can sometimes be used in
place of the primary function.

Why just "sometimes"?
Why not *always?*
If you're still not sure about this, then apparently we didn't make it clear.   The fact is that *either the primary or its reciprocal function can always be used to solve a problem involving a given combination of two sides and an angle.*   And this is so for the very simple reason that each pair of functions involves *exactly the same three parts* of the triangle!

Now return to page 28 and try again.

Your answer: I would choose the sin function.

Why?   Does it involve the use of the two known values, the lengths of sides *b* and *c*?   It must, you know, if it is to be of any help to us.   Otherwise we would wind up with a problem having *two unknowns* and only *one known* value.

What two sides does the sin function involve (with relation to angle *A*, of course)?   *Sides a and c*.   And what two sides are we concerned with?   *Sides b and c*.   Is anything wrong?   Obviously.   The sin function requires that we know the value of *side a* if we are to solve the problem through its use, and of course we *don't* know the length of side *a*.

The plain fact is you picked the wrong function.   So return to page 25 and select the right one.

Your answer: I would choose the cos function.

And you would be *right*, because the cosine function involves
the use of two *known* values,
namely, the lengths of sides
b and c.

Although we didn't offer you
the choice, it is important to recog-
nize that you could have used the secant instead of the cosine.
One is merely the reciprocal of the other and both involve the
same two sides of the triangle, sides b and c.

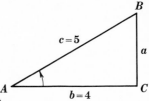

Actually, you always will have this choice.   That is, for any
given combination of two sides and one angle of a right triangle
you always have a choice between either a primary function
(sine, cosine, or tangent, as the case may be) or its reciprocal
(cosecant, secant, or cotangent).   Sometimes the reciprocal function works out a little more conveniently than the primary function; or, it may be just the other way around.

The general rule is that where there is no apparent advantage of one over the other, *choose the primary function.*

Are you clear on this point?   Let's see.

Select the statement below that best summarizes your understanding of what we have said above.

The reciprocal can always be used in place of
the primary function.   **PAGE 31**

The reciprocal can sometimes be used in place
of the primary function.   **PAGE 26**

I'm still not clear as to what you mean by "reciprocal."   **PAGE 33**

Your answer: I would choose the tan function.

If you did, you would be picking the wrong one. Why?
Because the only trigonometric function that is going to help
you is the one that involves the *two* sides whose lengths are
known.   True, we know the length of *side b,* but we don't know
the length of *side a.*

Now go back to page 25 and select the answer that will allow
us to use the two known values.

Your answer: It is the size of angle A in inches.

No, it's not.   But you're not alone in thinking this; it is a common misapprehension..

We don't measure the size of angles in inches or any other linear scale.   The sizes of angles are designated strictly in terms of degrees (°), minutes ('), and seconds (") of arc.   The word "arc," of course, refers to a section of a circle.   Thus angle sizes are stated in terms of *circular* measurement, and although there are other systems of circular measurement, the degrees-minutes-seconds system is the most common and the only one with which we will be concerned.

Incidentally, why inches?   Nothing was said about the lengths of the sides being in inches.   You must have inferred this.

In any case, return to page 31 and select a better answer.

Your answer: The reciprocal can always be used in place of the primary function.

Good! You got the point. I'm sure you realize we could have stated this the other way around, and it would have been just as true. That is, we could have said, "The *secondary function* (cosecant, secant, or cotangent) can always be used in place of *its reciprocal* (the primary function)." It all adds up to the same thing, namely, you can use either one in any given case.

Getting back to our triangle (shown here), we have agreed that, although either the cosine or secant could be used, we will follow the general rule of using the primary function where the choice is even. This gives us:

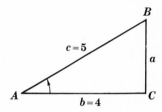

$$\cos A = \frac{b}{c}$$

and, by substitution of the given values,

$$\cos A = \frac{4}{5} = 0.8000$$

All that remains, therefore, is to discover what angle the value 0.8000 represents. To find this out, we refer to the table of Natural Trigonometric Functions (Appendix A, page 89), found at the back of the book.

Before delving into the table of natural trig functions, let's see if you're clear as to what the number 0.8000 represents. Select the correct statement below.

It simply represents the ratio of 4 to 5.   **PAGE 34**

It is the size of angle *A* in inches.   **PAGE 30**

I thought the size of angles was measured in degrees.   **PAGE 32**

Your answer: I thought the size of angles was measured in
                degrees.

And so it is.   You're right.   And we're going to get to this
matter of circular measurement in just a minute.   In the meantime, we'd like you to arrive at some conclusion in your own
mind as to just what the number 0.8000 represents.   How do
you think of it?   As a length, a volume, a simple ratio, or just
how?

Show us by picking another answer on page 31.

Your answer: I'm still not clear as to what you mean by "reciprocal."

Very well.   Let's have another go at explaining it.

When we first used the term, we added, parenthetically, "upside down version" in the hope that this would convey the idea if you hadn't come across the word before.   And this is basically what it means.

Perhaps a few examples will help.

$$\frac{3}{2} \text{ is the reciprocal of } \frac{2}{3}$$

$$\frac{a}{b} \text{ is the reciprocal of } \frac{b}{a}$$

$$\frac{\text{hypotenuse}}{\text{side } a} \text{ is the reciprocal of } \frac{\text{side } a}{\text{hypotenuse}}$$

Now return to page 28 and choose another answer.

Your answer: It simply represents the ratio of 4 to 5.

Good for you! You have arrived at the heart of the matter. It was obvious, you say? Fine; we're glad it was. It isn't to everyone, probably because we tend instinctively to assign some dimensional characteristic to most numbers, especially if they are related to other numbers that *do* have dimensional properties.

In this case, 4 over 5 is a ratio expressed as a simple fraction. If we divide 5 into 4, we arrive at the decimal fraction 0.8000, which represents the same ratio. Now we're ready to take that dive into the table of natural trigonometric functions (page 89) and to find out just what angle it is that the number 0.8000 represents.

Leaving the fingers of your left hand here to mark your place, turn to page 90 and observe the column labeled "cos." Notice that the cosine begins with a value of 1.00000 at 0° and *decreases* as the *angle increases.*

If we read down this column, turning the pages as we go, we arrive eventually at the value 0.80003, which is as close as we can come to 0.80000 without interpolation (look this last word up in the Glossary, page 80, if it is new to you), and note that the corresponding angular value is:

$A = 36°08'$ **PAGE 36**

$A = 53°08'$ **PAGE 35**

$A = 36°52'$ **PAGE 41**

Your answer: $A = 53°08'$

You're starting at the bottom of the page instead of the top! There will be times when it is appropriate to do this, and we will talk about some of them soon. But for now, remember that we started at the top of the first page of the table, noting that the cosine begins with a value of 1.00000 at 0° and decreases gradually as the angular value increases. And these *increasing* angular values are found along the *left* side of the table.

The angular values shown at the bottom and along the *right* side of the table (which you so shrewdly observed) should be ignored for the moment.

Return now to page 34 and select the correct answer.

Your answer: **A = 36°08′.**

Almost, but not quite.   The 36° is right, but the 08′ is wrong. Apparently you read your minutes value from the right-hand minute column, which happens to be located right next to the cosine column, instead of from the *left-hand* column, where you should have looked.

Look again, and then see if you can pick the correct answer on page 34.

′	sin	tan	cot	cos	
0	.58779	.72654	1.3764	.80902	60
1	802	699	.3755	885	59
2	826	743	.3747	867	58
3	849	788	.3739	850	57
4	873	832	.3730	833	56
5	.58896	.72877	1.3722	.80816	55
6	920	921	.3713	799	54
7	943	.72966	.3705	782	53
8	967	.73010	.3697	765	52
9	.58990	055	.3688	748	51
10	.59014	.73100	1.3680	.80730	50
11	037	144	.3672	713	49
12	061	189	.3663	696	48
13	084	234	.3655	679	47
14	108	278	.3647	662	46
15	.59131	.73323	1.3638	.80644	45
16	154	368	.3630	627	44
17	178	413	.3622	610	43
18	201	457	.3613	593	42
19	225	502	.3605	576	41
20	.59248	.73547	1.3597	.80558	40
21	272	592	.3588	541	39
22	295	637	.3580	524	38
23	318	681	.3572	507	37
24	342	726	.3564	489	36
25	.59365	.73771	1.3555	.80472	35
26	389	816	.3547	455	34
27	412	861	.3539	438	33
28	436	906	.3531	420	32
29	459	951	.3522	403	31
30	.59482	.73996	1.3514	.80386	30
31	506	74041	.3506	368	29
32	529	086	.3498	351	28
33	552	131	.3490	334	27
34	576	176	.3481	316	26
35	.59599	.74221	1.3473	.80299	25
36	622	267	.3465	282	24
37	646	312	.3457	264	23
38	669	357	.3449	247	22
39	693	402	.3440	230	21
40	.59716	.74447	1.3432	.80212	20
41	739	492	.3424	195	19
42	763	538	.3416	178	18
43	786	583	.3408	160	17
44	809	628	.3400	143	16
45	.59832	.74674	1.3392	.80125	15
46	856	719	.3384	108	14
47	879	764	.3375	091	13
48	902	810	.3367	073	12
49	926	855	.3359	056	11
50	.59949	.74900	1.3351	.80038	10
51	972	946	.3343	021	9
52	.59995	.74991	.3335	(80003)	(8)
53	.60019	.75037	.3327	.79986	7
54	042	082	.3319	968	6
55	.60065	.75128	1.3311	.79951	5
56	089	173	.3303	934	4
57	112	219	.3295	916	3
58	135	264	.3287	899	2
59	158	310	.3278	881	1
60	.60182	.75355	1.3270	.79864	0
	cos	cot	tan	sin	′

53°

′	sin	tan	cot	cos	
0	.60182	.75355	1.3270	.79864	60
1	205	401	.3262	846	59
2	228	447	.3254	829	58
3	251	492	.3246	811	57
4	274	538	.3238	793	56
5	.60298	.75584	1.3230	.79776	55
6	321	629	.3222	758	54
7	344	675	.3214	741	53
8	367	721	.3206	723	52
9	390	767	.3198	706	51
10	.60414	.75812	1.3190	.79688	50
11	437	858	.3182	671	49
12	460	904	.3175	653	48
13	483	950	.3167	635	47
14	506	.75996	.3159	618	46
15	.60529	.76042	1.3151	.79600	45
16	553	088	.3143	583	44
17	576	134	.3135	565	43
18	599	180	.3127	547	42
19	622	226	.3119	530	41
20	.60645	.76272	1.3111	.79512	40
21	668	318	.3103	494	39
22	691	364	.3095	477	38
23	714	410	.3087	459	37
24	738	456	.3079	441	36
25	.60761	.76502	1.3072	.79424	35
26	784	548	.3064	406	34
27	807	594	.3056	388	33
28	830	640	.3048	371	32
29	853	686	.3040	353	31
30	.60876	.76733	1.3032	.79335	30
31	899	779	.3024	318	29
32	922	825	.3017	300	28
33	945	871	.3009	282	27
34	968	918	.3001	264	26
35	.60991	.76964	1.2993	.79247	25
36	.61015	.77010	.2985	229	24
37	038	057	.2977	211	23
38	061	103	.2970	193	22
39	084	149	.2962	176	21
40	.61107	.77196	1.2954	.79158	20
41	130	242	.2946	140	19
42	153	289	.2938	122	18
43	176	335	.2931	105	17
44	199	382	.2923	087	16
45	.61222	.77428	1.2915	.79069	15
46	245	475	.2907	051	14
47	268	521	.2900	033	13
48	291	568	.2892	.79016	12
49	314	615	.2884	.78998	11
50	.61337	.77661	1.2876	.78980	10
51	360	708	.2869	962	9
52	383	754	.2861	944	8
53	406	801	.2853	926	7
54	429	848	.2846	908	6
55	.61451	.77895	1.2838	.78891	5
56	474	941	.2830	873	4
57	497	.77988	.2822	855	3
58	520	.78035	.2815	837	2
59	543	082	.2807	819	1
60	.61566	.78129	1.2799	.78801	0
	cos	cot	tan	sin	′

52°

Your answer: sin 53°08′ = 0.80003 (see previous page)

Very good. That's the correct answer, and you must have done everything right in order to have arrived at it. Do you recognize it as being the same as cos 36°52′? Now you know how to find the function values of angles greater than 45°. Practice a little more on your own, using random angular values of your own selection, and you will quickly master the tables of natural trigonometric functions.

Let's try another problem.

Suppose we know angle *B* and side *b*, but wish to find the length of side *a*. Again we must choose a trigonometric function involving the two known values, as well as the unknown value desired. For your convenience we're going to restate the six trigonometric functions below, *but this time in terms of angle B* (since that's our known angle this time), *rather than in terms of angle A*.

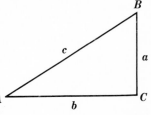

$$\sin B = \frac{b}{c} \qquad\qquad \csc B = \frac{c}{b}$$

$$\cos B = \frac{a}{c} \qquad\qquad \sec B = \frac{c}{a}$$

$$\tan B = \frac{b}{a} \qquad\qquad \cot B = \frac{a}{b}$$

With these functions in front of you, see if you can select the one most appropriate to the solution of the problem:

$\csc B = \dfrac{c}{b}$ **PAGE 42**

$\tan B = \dfrac{b}{a}$ **PAGE 44**

$\cot B = \dfrac{a}{b}$ **PAGE 46**

Your answer: sin 53°08′ = 0.58967

Well, you're on the right page!   And in the right table—but the wrong column.   Because the angle we gave you was over 45°, we have to look for our angle values at the *bottom* of each table, instead of at the top; and you did this correctly, since you wound up in the right table.

However, instead of looking for the "sin" heading at the *bottom* of the columns (as we must when our angle is *greater* than 45°), you looked (probably automatically) at the top of the table, then found your minutes value (08′) in the *left*-hand, instead of in the *right*-hand, column where you should have looked.   What you really found, therefore, was the sine of 36°08′.

I'm sure you have a better notion now of what to do, so look again; then turn back to page 41 and choose the correct answer.

′	sin	tan	cot	cos	
0	.58779	.72654	1.3764	.80902	60
1	802	699	.3755	885	59
2	826	743	.3747	867	58
3	849	788	.3739	850	57
4	873	832	.3730	833	56
5	.58896	.72877	1.3722	.80816	55
6	920	921	.3713	799	54
7	943	.72966	.3705	782	53
8	967	.73010	.3697	765	52
9	.58990	055	.3688	748	51
10	.59014	.73100	1.3680	.80730	50
11	037	144	.3672	713	49
12	061	189	.3663	696	48
13	084	234	.3655	679	47
14	108	278	.3647	662	46
15	.59131	.73323	1.3638	.80644	45
16	154	368	.3630	627	44
17	178	413	.3622	610	43
18	201	457	.3613	593	42
19	225	502	.3605	576	41
20	.59248	.73547	1.3597	.80558	40
21	272	592	.3588	541	39
22	295	637	.3580	524	38
23	318	681	.3572	507	37
24	342	726	.3564	489	36
25	.59365	.73771	1.3555	.80472	35
26	389	816	.3547	455	34
27	412	861	.3539	438	33
28	436	906	.3531	420	32
29	459	951	.3522	403	31
30	.59482	.73996	1.3514	.80386	30
31	506	74041	.3506	368	29
32	529	086	.3498	351	28
33	552	131	.3490	334	27
34	576	176	.3481	316	26
35	.59599	.74221	1.3473	.80299	25
36	622	267	.3465	282	24
37	646	312	.3457	264	23
38	669	357	.3449	247	22
39	693	402	.3440	230	21
40	.59716	.74447	1.3432	.80212	20
41	739	492	.3424	195	19
42	763	538	.3416	178	18
43	786	583	.3408	160	17
44	809	628	.3400	143	16
45	.59832	.74674	1.3392	.80125	15
46	856	719	.3384	108	14
47	879	764	.3375	091	13
48	902	810	.3367	073	12
49	926	855	.3359	056	11
50	.59949	.74900	1.3351	.80038	10
51	972	946	.3343	021	9
52	.59995	.74991	1.3335	.80003	8
53	.60019	.75037	.3327	.79986	7
54	042	082	.3319	968	6
55	.60065	.75128	1.3311	.79951	5
56	089	173	.3303	934	4
57	112	219	.3295	916	3
58	135	264	.3287	899	2
59	158	310	.3278	881	1
60	.60182	.75355	1.3270	.79864	0
	cos	cot	tan	sin	′

′	sin	tan	cot	cos	
0	.60182	.75355	1.3270	.79864	60
1	205	401	.3262	846	59
2	228	447	.3254	829	58
3	251	492	.3246	811	57
4	274	538	.3238	793	56
5	.60298	.75584	1.3230	.79776	55
6	321	629	.3222	758	54
7	344	675	.3214	741	53
8	367	721	.3206	723	52
9	390	767	.3198	706	51
10	.60414	.75812	1.3190	.79688	50
11	437	858	.3182	671	49
12	460	904	.3175	653	48
13	483	950	.3167	635	47
14	506	.75996	.3159	618	46
15	.60529	.76042	1.3151	.79600	45
16	553	088	.3143	583	44
17	576	134	.3135	565	43
18	599	180	.3127	547	42
19	622	226	.3119	530	41
20	.60645	.76272	1.3111	.79512	40
21	668	318	.3103	494	39
22	691	364	.3095	477	38
23	714	410	.3087	459	37
24	738	456	.3079	441	36
25	.60761	.76502	1.3072	.79424	35
26	784	548	.3064	406	34
27	807	594	.3056	388	33
28	830	640	.3048	371	32
29	853	686	.3040	353	31
30	.60876	.76733	1.3032	.79335	30
31	899	779	.3024	318	29
32	922	825	.3017	300	28
33	945	871	.3009	282	27
34	968	918	.3001	264	26
35	.60991	.76964	1.2993	.79247	25
36	.61015	.77010	.2985	229	24
37	038	057	.2977	211	23
38	061	103	.2970	193	22
39	084	149	.2962	176	21
40	.61107	.77196	1.2954	.79158	20
41	130	242	.2946	140	19
42	153	289	.2938	122	18
43	176	335	.2931	105	17
44	199	382	.2923	087	16
45	.61222	.77428	1.2915	.79069	15
46	245	475	.2907	051	14
47	268	521	.2900	033	13
48	291	568	.2892	.79016	12
49	314	615	.2884	.78998	11
50	.61337	.77661	1.2876	.78980	10
51	360	708	.2869	962	9
52	383	754	.2861	944	8
53	406	801	.2853	926	7
54	429	848	.2846	908	6
55	.61451	.77895	1.2838	.78891	5
56	474	941	.2830	873	4
57	497	.77988	.2822	855	3
58	520	.78035	.2815	837	2
59	543	082	.2807	819	1
60	.61566	.78129	1.2799	.78801	0
	cos	cot	tan	sin	′

Your answer: $A = 36°52''$ (See preceding page)

Absolutely correct!   We purposely didn't give you much help as you found your way through these tables because we thought you might like to see how well you could do by yourself; and you did very well indeed.

However, there's something you should know at this point if you have not used trig tables before.   In order to save space, publishers take advantage of the fact that the sine and *co*sine (also the tangent and *co*tangent, secant and *co*secant) are what we call "co-functions."   We will go into the matter of just what a co-function is a little later.   For now, it is sufficient to point out that the sine of an angle is numerically equal to the *co*sine of 90° minus the angle; the tangent of an angle is equal to *co*tangent of 90° minus the angle; and the secant is equal to the *co*secant of 90° minus the angle.

This means that, to cover the entire range of natural trigonometric functions up to 90°, the publisher only has to print tables ranging up to 45°.   Beyond 45°, he merely has to change the function names at the bottom of the columns, print the degree values at the bottom of the page, reverse the minute values to read *up* instead of down (along the right-hand edge), and the job is done.

Just for a little more practice, try looking up the sine of 53°08′.

sin 53°08′ = 0.58967	**PAGE 39**
sin 53°08′ = 0.80003	**PAGE 38**
sin 53°08′ = 0.59995	**PAGE 43**

Your answer: $\csc B = \dfrac{c}{b}$

No, this would enable you to find the length of side c but not of side a, which is the side we want.   Notice that side a doesn't even appear in the above equation; hence we can hardly hope to find something that isn't there!

If we expect to discover the length of side a, we *must* select an expression that contains a as a factor and that *also* contains the two *known* values.   With this in mind, go back to page 38 and select a better answer.

Your answer: sin 53°08′ = 0.59995

No, I'm afraid you misfired.   You're close, but being close is not good enough in mathematics, a branch of learning where a miss is as good as a mile.

You are on the right page, which means you remembered to look for angle values at the bottom (rather than the top) of the tables.   And you are on the right *line,* which indicates that you also remembered to read your minute values in the right-hand minute column, starting at the bottom.

What's wrong then?   Apparently, at the last moment, when looking for the column headings to find the "sin" column, you looked *up* at the names across the top, rather than *down* at the names along the bottom, and so got in the wrong column.   What you actually found, therefore, was the *cosine* of 53°08′.

Get in the right column this time, and then see if your answer doesn't match up with another (the correct) answer on page 41.

Your answer: $\tan B = \dfrac{b}{a}$

Yes, this is a perfectly good choice, for it contains the two known values, as well as the unknown value (side a) we are seeking. Either the tangent or cotangent would serve, since both contain the three necessary terms. Although it may not be apparent to you at the moment, the cotangent actually will be a little easier to use from the standpoint of solving the equation, since it will involve less algebraic "juggling" (transposition of terms).

To see what we mean, and just how this will work out, go back to page 38 and choose the cotangent function.

Your answer: cot 52°18′ = 1.2938

You looked in the tangent column!   You found the 52° table all right, and the correct row for 18′ of arc.   But either you used the cot heading at the top or else you didn't look closely enough at the headings at the bottom.   In either case, you strayed into the wrong column.

Try again to see if you can't select the correct answer on page 46.

Your answer: $\cot B = \dfrac{a}{b}$

You are to be congratulated if you chose this answer the first time. Actually, either the tangent or cotangent function would serve to give us the solution to the problem, but use of the cotangent will simplify the work somewhat. Therefore we set the problem up as follows:

$$\cot B = \frac{\text{adjacent side}}{\text{opposite side}} = \frac{a}{b}$$

Hence, by the substitution of the known values shown in the drawing here,

$B = 52°18'$
$b = 12$
$a = ?$

$$\cot 52°18' = \frac{a}{12}$$

or, by transposition,

$$a = 12 \times \cot 52°18'$$

Since in algebra the times sign ($\times$) is omitted, this equation may be written simply

$$a = 12 \cot 52°18'$$

In other words, to solve the equation for a, we must multiply 12 times the cotangent of $52°18'$. But what is the cotangent of $52°18'$? Look it up in your table of trigonometric functions. What you find should enable you to select the correct answer below.

$\cot 52°18' = 0.77289$ **PAGE 49**

$\cot 52°18' = 1.2938$ **PAGE 45**

$\cot 52°18' = 1.3127$ **PAGE 47**

Your answer: cot 52°18′ = 1.3127

It looks as though you made the mistake of reading your minutes value down from the top, in the left-hand column, and used the corresponding cotangent value.   At least you are in the correct (52°) table.

Remember, for angles over 45°, you not only locate the table by reference to the degree values shown at the *bottom* of each table, but you also must use the right-hand minute column, reading up from the bottom.   Having done this, use the column headings *at the bottom* to make certain you're pursuing the proper function; then read across to your answer.

Try again; I'm sure you'll have no trouble this time.   With the information you get, look back at page 46 and choose the right answer.

′	sin	tan	cot	cos	
0	.58779	.72654	1.3764	.80902	60
1	802	699	.3755	885̄	59
2	826	743	.3747	867	58
3	849	788	.3739	850	57
4	873	832	.3730	833	56
5	.58896	.72877	1.3722	.80816	55
6	920	921	.3713	799	54
7	943	72966	.3705	782	53
8	967	.73010	.3697	765̄	52
9	.58990	055	.3688	748	51
10	.59014	.73100	1.3680	.80730	50
11	037	144	.3672	713	49
12	061	189	.3663	696	48
13	084	234	.3655	679	47
14	108	278	.3647	662	46
15	.59131	.73323	1.3638	.80644	45
16	154	368	.3630	627	44
17	178	413	.3622	610	43
18	201	457	.3613	593	42
19	225̄	502	.3605	576	41
20	.59248	.73547	1.3597	.80558	40
21	272	592	.3588	541	39
22	295	637	.3580	524	38
23	318	681	.3572	507	37
24	342	726	.3564	489	36
25	.59365	.73771	1.3555	.80472	35
26	389	816	.3547	455̄	34
27	412	861	.3539	438	33
28	436	906	.3531	420	32
29	459	951	.3522	403	31
30	.59482	.73996	1.3514	.80386	30
31	506	74041	.3506	368	29
32	529	086	.3498	351	28
33	552	131	.3490	334	27
34	576	176	.3481	316	26
35	.59599	.74221	1.3473	.80299	25
36	622	267	.3465	282	24
37	646	312	.3457	264	23
38	669	357	.3449	247	22
39	693	402	.3440	230	21
40	.59716	.74447	1.3432	.80212	20
41	739	492	.3424	195	19
42	763	538	.3416	178	18
43	786	583	.3408	160	17
44	809	628	.3400	143	16
45	.59832	.74674	1.3392	.80125	15
46	856	719	.3384	108	14
47	879	764	.3375	091	13
48	902	810	.3367	073	12
49	926	855̄	.3359	056	11
50	.59949	.74900	1.3351	.80038	10
51	972	946	.3343	021	9
52	.59995	.74991	.3335̄	.80003	8
53	.60019	.75037	.3327	.79986	7
54	042	082	.3319	968	6
55	.60065	.75128	1.3311	.79951	5
56	089	173	.3303	934	4
57	112	219	.3295̄	916	3
58	135	264	.3287	899	2
59	158	310	.3278	881	1
60	.60182	.75355	1.3270	.79864	0
	cos	cot	tan	sin	′

53°

′	sin	tan	cot	cos	
0	.60182	.75355	1.3270	.79864	60
1	205̄	401	.3262	846	59
2	228	447	.3254	829	58
3	251	492	.3246	811	57
4	274	538	.3238	793	56
5	.60298	.75584	1.3230	.79776	55
6	321	629	.3222	758	54
7	344	675	.3214	741	53
8	367	721	.3206	723	52
9	390	767	.3198	706	51
10	.60414	.75812	1.3190	.79688	50
11	437	858	.3182	671	49
12	460	904	.3175	653	48
13	483	950	.3167	635	47
14	506	.75996	.3159	618	46
15	.60529	.76042	1.3151	.79600	45
16	553	088	.3143	583	44
17	576	134	.3135	565̄	43
18	599	180	.3127	547	42
19	622	226	.3119	530	41
20	.60645	.76272	1.3111	.79512	40
21	668	318	.3103	494	39
22	691	364	.3095	477	38
23	714	410	.3087	459	37
24	738	456	.3079	441	36
25	.60761	.76502	1.3072	.79424	35
26	784	548	.3064	406	34
27	807	594	.3056	388	33
28	830	640	.3048	371	32
29	853	686	.3040	353	31
30	.60876	.76733	1.3032	.79335	30
31	899	779	.3024	318	29
32	922	825	.3017	300	28
33	945	871	.3009	282	27
34	968	918	.3001	264	26
35	.60991	.76964	1.2993	.79247	25
36	.61015̄	.77010	.2985	229	24
37	038	057	.2977	211	23
38	061	103	.2970	193	22
39	084	149	.2962	176	21
40	.61107	.77196	1.2954	.79158	20
41	130	242	.2946	140	19
42	153	289	.2938	122	18
43	176	335̄	.2931	105̄	17
44	199	382	.2923	087	16
45	.61222	.77428	1.2915	.79069	15
46	245̄	475̄	.2907	051	14
47	268	521	.2900	033	13
48	291	568	.2892	.79016	12
49	314	615̄	.2884	.78998	11
50	.61337	.77661	1.2876	.78980	10
51	360	708	.2869	962	9
52	383	754	.2861	944	8
53	406	801	.2853	926	7
54	429	848	.2846	908	6
55	.61451	.77895̄	1.2838	.78891	5
56	474	941	.2830	873	4
57	497	.77988	.2822	855̄	3
58	520	.78035̄	.2815	837	2
59	543	082	.2807	819	1
60	.61566	.78129	1.2799	.78801	0
	cos	cot	tan	sin	′

52°

542

Your answer: cot 52°18′ = 0.77289 (See preceding page)

Correct.   With every one of these values you look up, you will find it easier to use the trig tables.

Our equation was, as you will recall,

$$a = 12 \cot 52°18′$$

Now that we know the value of the cotangent, we can substitute as follows:

$$a = 12 \ (0.77289)$$

or

$$a = 9.27$$

"Yes, but 9.27 *what?*" you ask.   We answer, 9.27 *anything* (any kind of *linear* measurement, that is) you like: feet, inches, furlongs, Spanish miles, centimeters—the choice is up to you.   If no unit was specified (and it wasn't in this case) when giving you the length of side b, then you can think of both side a and side b as being in any convenient unit of measurement.   Usually, in a practical problem, the type of unit *would* be specified, and of course, all sides would be in the same units, whether they were feet, inches, or whatever.

Well, wasn't that easy?

Now, what would you like to know next?

I need help on this business of transposition.   **PAGE 51**

I'd like to see another example.   **PAGE 58**

I'd like to work some problems.   **PAGE 62**

I'm ready to move on.   **PAGE 67**

Your answer: I would divide both sides by 3.

I'm afraid this wouldn't help, but let's try it anyway just so you'll see:

$$\frac{x-3}{3} = \frac{5}{3}$$

Doesn't give you much, does it?   We're no closer to, perhaps even further away from, the solution than we were originally.

Return to page 51 and select another answer.

Your answer: I need help on this business of transposition.

Don't feel bad if you wound up on this page; you've probably got a lot of company!   The process of moving numbers back and forth across the equal (=) sign of an equation, called "transposition," is one that seems to baffle many people.   Yet it's really quite simple.   Let's take a look at it.

Terms, that is, numbers and letters, appearing on either side of an equal sign are linked together (or separated from each other, depending on how you want to think of it) by one of four symbols: a plus (+) sign, a minus (−) sign, a multiplication sign (written or understood), or a dividing sign (fraction bar).

Now *the "golden rule" that applies to the shifting about of the terms of an equation is this: whatever you do to one side you must do to the other.*   What does this mean?   It means that you can *add* the same amount to both sides of the equation, *subtract* the same amount from both sides of the equation, or *multiply* or *divide* both sides of the equation by the same quantity without upsetting the equality.

How does this work in practice?   Let's see.

Suppose you have this equation:

$$x - 3 = 5$$

To "solve" the equation we must get the x on one side (usually the left) by itself, and the other terms (numbers) all on the right side.   How would you go about solving it?

I would subtract 3 from both sides.	**PAGE 53**
I would divide both sides by 3.	**PAGE 50**
I would add 3 to both sides.	**PAGE 52**

Your answer: I would add 3 to both sides.

Exactly right!   And why?   Because this has the effect of removing the −3 from the left side and transposing it to the right side where we want it.   Thus

$$x - 3 + 3 = 5 + 3$$

or, since the +3 and −3 cancel each other on the left side,

$$x = 8$$

which is our answer.

Now notice that this is exactly the same result we would have obtained by moving the −3 in our original equation to the right side and changing its sign from − to +.

This gives us a rule: *A term may be transposed from one side of an equation to the other if its sign is changed from + to − or from − to +.*   Therefore, whenever the terms of an equation are separated by a + or − sign, all you have to do in order to transpose one (or more) of these terms across the = sign is to reverse its sign and move it to the other side.   What could be simpler?

Just to test your understanding of this rule, try solving the problem below.

$$7 + y = 16$$

$$y = \underline{\hspace{1cm}}$$

Turn to page 55 for the correct answer.

Your answer: I would subtract 3 from both sides.

Well, let's take a look at what you would get if you did so.
Your equation would then look like this:

$$x - 3 - 3 = 5 - 3$$

or

$$x - 6 = 2$$

Has subtracting 3 from both sides solved the equation?
Obviously not, so this must not be the correct method.

Return to page 51 and try again.

Your answer: I would divide both sides by S.

Good for you!   I hope you chose this answer because you saw what dividing both sides by S would do.   Let's see.

$$\frac{D}{S} = \frac{T \times S}{S}$$

Beautiful, isn't it?   The two S's cancel out on the right side leaving T by itself, just as we wanted, and the S now appears in the *denominator* of the left-hand term.

It was pointed out earlier that we usually try to wind up with the unknown term on the left side of the equation; however, this is merely a convention and obviously doesn't affect the correctness of the solution.   If we wish to do this as a final step in the above example, we have only to switch the terms on both sides of the equation to the opposite sides (where they are still just as equal to each other), and we then have

$$T = \frac{D}{S}$$

As an obvious corollary to the above, if we had started out with the relationship

$$T = \frac{D}{S}$$

and wanted to solve for D, we would have to *multiply* both sides of the equation by S, thus canceling out the S in the denominator of the right-hand term and making it a multiplier of T; thus

$$T \times S = \frac{D \times S}{S}$$

or $$D = T \times S$$

(transposing both terms), and we have our original equation.

Our rule then: A factor (multiplier) may be removed from one side of an equation by making it a divisor in the other.   A divisor may be removed from one side of an equation by making it a factor (multiplier) in the other.

For one more example, this time from trigonometry, turn to page 56.

Correct answer: $y = 9$

Good! Now how did you get this answer? You *should* have arrived at it by changing the sign of the 7 from $+$ to $-$ and moving it across the $=$ sign to the right side of the equation. *But remember,* our *justification* for doing this lies in the fact that what we *really* are doing is subtracting the same amount (7) from *both* sides of the equation, which has the *effect* of transposing a -7 to the right side without upsetting the existing equality.

Now, how about the problem of transposing terms that are factors (multipliers) or dividers? It's just as simple.

As an example, let's take the relationship that exists between time, speed, and distance (T, S, and D). We know that distance equals time multiplied by speed, which gives us the mathematical relationship

$$D = T \times S$$

But supposing we have a problem in which we know distance and speed and therefore wish to solve for time. This will require that we rewrite or transpose the equation in such a way that T (the unknown term) is by itself on one side of the $=$ sign and the two known values, S and D, are on the other side.

Remembering that the "golden rule" of algebra allows us to multiply or divide both sides of an equation by the same term, do you have any idea how we might go about accomplishing the transposition we need? What would you do?

I would multiply both sides by S.	**PAGE 57**
I would divide both sides by S.	**PAGE 54**
I would subtract S from both sides.	**PAGE 59**

Perhaps you have forgotten by now that the problem which brought up this matter of transposition was the example on page 46 where we had the following equation:

$$\cot 52°18' = \frac{a}{12}$$

Do you see now how we were able to transpose this to the relationship

$$a = 12 \times \cot 52°18'$$

or just

$$a = 12 \cot 52°18'$$

(omitting the times sign as we usually do in algebra)?

What did we do?   Multiplied both sides by 12?   Absolutely correct!   This resulted in canceling out the 12 in the denominator of the right-hand term and inserting it as a factor in the left-hand term, then (just to follow convention) transposing *both* terms to opposite sides so we would wind up with our unknown quantity *a* on the left side.

With this explanation of the rules of transposition, let's return to page 49 where you may choose the next step you wish to take.

Your answer: I would multiply both sides by S.

Why?
Let's see what this would give you.

$$D \times S = T \times S \times S$$

or

$$D \times S = T \times S^2$$

It doesn't look much like a solution, does it?

You must be guessing.   Turn back to page 55, re-read the explanation given there, and then choose another answer.

Your answer: I'd like to see another example.

Very well.   Let's try another one that involves finding an angular value.

Consider the triangle shown. The lengths of two sides are given, and if necessary, we could find the length of the third side by use of the theory of Pythagoras (remember from geometry?).   But this wouldn't help us find out how big the *angles* are.   So, turning to trigonometry for help, we first have to select a function that includes the two known quantities (lengths of the two sides) plus one of the unknown angles—angle A, for instance.

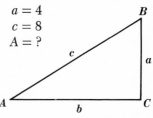

$a = 4$
$c = 8$
$A = ?$

What equation, or function, could you use?

Only the cosecant of *A*.   **PAGE 61**

Either the sine or the cosecant of angle *A*.   **PAGE 64**

The tangent of *A* would be best to use.   **PAGE 60**

Your answer: I would subtract S from both sides.

No, this is just about the one thing you most certainly should *not* do.   *Remember:* The terms of *this* equation are not separated by + or − signs but are *factors* and therefore separated by a *multiplication* sign!   Hence the rules for transposing added or subtracted terms do not apply.

There is a better answer, so (even though we haven't told you what it is) see if you can't pick it out on page 55.

Your answer: The tangent of A would be best to use.

On the contrary, it would be impossible to use, at least if you expected to arrive at any kind of an answer.   Your high school beginning algebra course, I'm sure, taught you that one equation will only permit you to solve for one unknown; if you used the tangent, you'd have *two* unknown quantities: angle *A* and side *b*.

Bear in mind, always, that you must choose a function that contains the *two known* elements and *only one unknown* term. With this thought in mind return to page 58 and make a better choice.

Your answer: Only the cosecant of **A.**

Why only the cosecant?   You're on the right track; that is, you've selected a function that will fulfill the mathematical requirements for a correct solution, insofar as it combines the two known quantities with the unknown value (angle *A*) we are seeking.   But isn't there another function that involves these same three terms?

Think about it, and then return to page 58 to select the correct answer.

Your answer: I'd like to work some problems.

Very well, here you are.

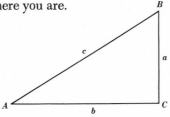

1. $a = 6.4$ ft, $b = 6.4$ ft, $A = \underline{\hspace{1.5cm}}$
2. $b = 12$ in, $A = 15°39'$, $c = \underline{\hspace{1.5cm}}$
3. $b = 27.1$ miles, $c = 29.1$ miles, $B = \underline{\hspace{1.5cm}}$

4. A mountain climber stretches a rope from the top of a sheer cliff to a point on the level ground below, making an angle of 48° with the ground. If the rope is 86 feet long, how high is the cliff?
Ans._____

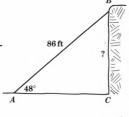

5. A 34-foot ladder is placed against the side of a house with the foot of the ladder 9 feet away from the building. What angle does the ladder make with the ground?
Ans._____

6. In order to find the breadth of a river, a distance AB was measured along the bank, the point A being directly opposite a tree C on the other side. If the angle at B was observed to be 40° and the distance AB 100 feet, how wide was the river? Ans._____

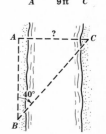

For answers please turn to page 65.

'	sin	tan	cot	cos	'
0	.50000	.57735	1.7321	.86603	60
1	025	774	.7309	588	59
2	050	813	.7297	573	58
3	076	851	.7286	559	57
4	101	890	.7274	544	56
5	.50126	.57929	1.7262	.86530	55
6	151	.57968	.7251	515	54
7	176	.58007	.7239	501	53
8	201	046	.7228	486	52
9	227	085	.7216	471	51
10	.50252	.58124	1.7205	.86457	50
11	277	162	.7193	442	49
12	302	201	.7182	427	48
13	327	240	.7170	413	47
14	352	279	.7159	398	46
15	.50377	.58318	1.7147	.86384	45
16	403	357	.7136	369	44
17	428	396	.7124	354	43
18	453	435	.7113	340	42
19	478	474	.7102	325	41
20	.50503	.58513	1.7090	.86310	40
21	528	552	.7079	295	39
22	553	591	.7067	281	38
23	578	631	.7056	266	37
24	603	670	.7045	251	36
25	.50628	.58709	1.7033	.86237	35
26	654	748	.7022	222	34
27	679	787	.7011	207	33
28	704	826	.6999	192	32
29	729	865	.6988	178	31
30	.50754	.58905	1.6977	.86163	30
31	779	944	.6965	148	29
32	804	.58983	.6954	133	28
33	829	.59022	.6943	119	27
34	854	061	.6932	104	26
35	.50879	.59101	1.6920	.86089	25
36	904	140	.6909	074	24
37	929	179	.6898	059	23
38	954	218	.6887	045	22
39	.50979	258	.6875	030	21
40	.51004	.59297	1.6864	.86015	20
41	029	336	.6853	.86000	19
42	054	376	.6842	.85985	18
43	079	415	.6831	970	17
44	104	454	.6820	956	16
45	.51129	.59494	1.6808	.85941	15
46	154	533	.6797	926	14
47	179	573	.6786	911	13
48	204	612	.6775	896	12
49	229	651	.6764	881	11
50	.51254	.59691	1.6753	.85866	10
51	279	730	.6742	851	9
52	304	770	.6731	836	8
53	329	809	.6720	821	7
54	354	849	.6709	806	6
55	.51379	.59888	1.6698	.85792	5
56	404	928	.6687	777	4
57	429	.59967	.6676	762	3
58	454	.60007	.6665	747	2
59	479	046	.6654	732	1
60	.51504	.60086	1.6643	.85717	0
'	cos	cot	tan	sin	

59°

'	sin	tan	cot	cos	'
0	.51504	.60086	1.6643	.85717	60
1	529	126	.6632	702	59
2	554	165	.6621	687	58
3	579	205	.6610	672	57
4	604	245	.6599	657	56
5	.51628	.60284	1.6588	.85642	55
6	653	324	.6577	627	54
7	678	364	.6566	612	53
8	703	403	.6555	597	52
9	728	443	.6545	582	51
10	.51753	.60483	1.6534	.85567	50
11	778	522	.6523	551	49
12	803	562	.6512	536	48
13	828	602	.6501	521	47
14	852	642	.6490	506	46
15	.51877	.60681	1.6479	.85491	45
16	902	721	.6469	476	44
17	927	761	.6458	461	43
18	952	801	.6447	446	42
19	.51977	841	.6436	431	41
20	.52002	.60881	1.6426	.85416	40
21	026	921	.6415	401	39
22	051	.60960	.6404	385	38
23	076	.61000	.6393	370	37
24	101	040	.6383	355	36
25	.52126	.61080	1.6372	.85340	35
26	151	120	.6361	325	34
27	175	160	.6351	310	33
28	200	200	.6340	294	32
29	225	240	.6329	279	31
30	.52250	.61280	1.6319	.85264	30
31	275	320	.6308	249	29
32	299	360	.6297	234	28
33	324	400	.6287	218	27
34	349	440	.6276	203	26
35	.52374	.61480	1.6265	.85188	25
36	399	520	.6255	173	24
37	423	561	.6244	157	23
38	448	601	.6234	142	22
39	473	641	.6223	127	21
40	.52498	.61681	1.6212	.85112	20
41	522	721	.6202	096	19
42	547	761	.6191	081	18
43	572	801	.6181	066	17
44	597	842	.6170	051	16
45	.52621	.61882	1.6160	.85035	15
46	646	922	.6149	020	14
47	671	.61962	.6139	.85005	13
48	696	.62003	.6128	.84989	12
49	720	043	.6118	974	11
50	.52745	.62083	1.6107	.84959	10
51	770	124	.6097	943	9
52	794	164	.6087	928	8
53	819	204	.6076	913	7
54	844	245	.6066	897	6
55	.52869	.62285	1.6055	.84882	5
56	893	325	.6045	866	4
57	918	366	.6034	851	3
58	943	406	.6024	836	2
59	967	446	.6014	820	1
60	.52992	.62487	1.6003	.84805	0
'	cos	cot	tan	sin	

58°

Your answer: Either the sine or the cosecant of angle A.

Good thinking; you're quite right.   Both the sine and cosecant functions (being reciprocals) make use of the two known terms and also include, of course, the unknown quantity angle A.

Having narrowed our choice down to two instead of six functions, we have only to choose between the two.   And, since there is no real preference in this case (from the standpoint of making the work easier), we follow our basic rule of selecting the primary function when the choice is even.   Our equation therefore becomes

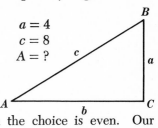

$a = 4$
$c = 8$
$A = ?$

$$\sin A = \frac{a}{c}$$

or, substituting,

$$\sin A = \frac{4}{8} = 0.50000$$

To look up the angular value of A corresponding to a sine value of 0.50000, we begin at the beginning, noting that the sine of 0° is zero but that it gradually increases as we proceed into higher angular values.   Continuing, then, we come eventually to the sine value of 0.50000 and find it opposite 30°.   Hence the solution to our problem:

$A = 30°$ (see preceding page)

Please return to page 49 and make another choice.

Answers to problems appearing on page 62.

1. $\tan A = \dfrac{a}{b} = \dfrac{6.4}{6.4} = 1.0000$; $A = 45°$

2. $\cos A = \dfrac{b}{c}$, $\quad c = \dfrac{b}{\cos A}$, $\quad c = \dfrac{12}{0.96293} = 12.5$ in

3. $\sin B = \dfrac{b}{c} = \dfrac{27.1}{29.1} = 0.93127$; $B = 68°38'$

4. $\sin A = \dfrac{a}{c}$, $\quad a = c \sin A = 86 \sin 48° = 86\,(0.74314)$;
   $a = 63.9$ ft

5. $\cos A = \dfrac{b}{c} = \dfrac{9}{34} = 0.26471$; $A = 74°39'$

6. $\tan B = \dfrac{AC}{AB}$, $AC = AB \tan B = 100 \tan 40°$
   $= 100\,(0.83910)$; $AC = 83.9$ ft

Note: Those who feel the need for some additional practice solving problems in trigonometry will find it on page 84.

Please turn to page 49 and make another choice.

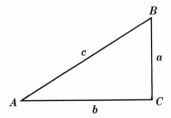

Another way of approaching this matter of co-functions is to remember that the sum of angles A and B is 90°; hence they are complementary angles. The term "complementary," which you may recall from geometry, means that two angles add up to 90°. We know that the sum of the angles in a plane triangle is 180°; hence in a right triangle the sum of the two acute angles must equal 90°. Therefore, if angle A has a certain value, then the value of angle B must be $90° - A$. Conversely, the value of angle A (if angle B is known) is $90° - B$.

We come, then, to the interesting conclusion that

$$\sin A = \cos B$$

or since

$$B = 90° - A$$

$$\sin A = \cos (90° - A)$$

Hence

$$\tan A = \cot B$$

$$= \cot (90° - A)$$

and

$$\sec A = \csc B$$

$$= \csc (90° - A)$$

And the same equations could be derived for angle B. Now do you understand why the tables of natural trigonometric functions only need be calculated as far as 45°?

Yes   **PAGE 69**

No   **PAGE 68**

Your answer: I'm ready to move on.

Very well.   Since it is the purpose of this book only to help the reader gain a familiarity with the trigonometric functions— what they are and, briefly, how they are used—no further illustrative problems will be introduced.   Any number of good problems may be found in trigonometry textbooks.

However, there is one more basic concept with which the student should become familiar before leaving the subject of plane trigonometry.   That is the matter of "co-functions," which we touched upon earlier.

Referring back mentally to the list of trigonometric functions, it will be noted that basically the six terms bear only three names, the other three names being formed by the prefix "co."   Thus there is the

sine and *co*sine

tangent and *co*tangent

secant and *co*secant

The cosine is said to be the co-function of the sine; the cotangent the co-function of the tangent; and the cosecant the co-function of the secant.   What the term "co-function" means can best be shown by an example.

In the figure shown here, sin $A = a/c$, but cos B also equals a/c. Thus angle B is said to be a *co-function* of angle A and vice versa.

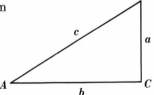

Proceed on page 66.

Your answer: No

Well, that's a good, direct answer.   Let's see if we can't make our explanation equally direct.

We have established that since angles A and B add up to 90° (as they always must in a right triangle), they are complementary (by definition) and are said to be co-functions of one another. That is, any function of one is equal to the *co-function* of the other.   This gives us the relationships shown on the preceding page:

$$\sin A = \cos B$$

$$\tan A = \cot B$$

$$\sec A = \csc B$$

Think of what this means.   Take sin A, for instance, and suppose A is 30°.   Then we are saying that sin 30° equals cos B; *but* angle B, being the complement of angle A, is equal to *90° minus angle A.*   Hence angle B is 60°.   Therefore, what we are really saying is

$$\sin 30° = \cos 60°$$

But sin 30° is a definite numerical quantity.   If we look up its value in the trig tables we find it to be 0.50000.   And since sin 30° = cos 60°, we should expect that cos 60° *also* equals 0.50000.   And so it does!   Obviously there is no need to print this function value of 0.50000 more than once to suit the needs of both the sin and cos in this case.

And so it goes throughout the tables for all sin and cos values. And the same thing applies to the tan and cot functions and to the sec and csc functions.

Please return to page 66 and choose the other answer.

Your answer: Yes

Good!   If you see this then you understand the concept of co-functions and complementary angles we've been talking about.

Another handy way to remember it is to keep in mind that the value of the functions and co-functions move in exactly opposite directions, numerically, when angles increase from 0° to 90° or decrease from 90° to 0°.   Thus the sine *increases* in value from 0 at 0° to 1 at 90°.   It is apparent, therefore, that these function values pass each other at the halfway mark, namely, 45°.   After 45°, we find our *cosine* values in the *sin* column, reading *up* the sin column from the bottom (as the angle increases) instead of down from the top.   Conversely, we find our *sine* values in the *cos* column, again reading up from the bottom.

This nearly completes our discussion of plane trigonometry. But before leaving the subject—and while it is still fresh in our minds—we'd better take a last look back to make sure we remember the most important points.

If you'll turn to page 70, we'll begin a quick review.

Review of Trigonometry

1. The kind of trigonometry we're talking about in this book, *plane* trigonometry, deals with the relationships existing between the sides and angles of plane triangles.

2. A "plane" triangle is one whose sides are straight lines lying in the same plane.

3. A plane (in the mathematical sense of the word) is a two-dimensional (flat) surface.

4. Trigonometry (and when we use the word by itself we mean *plane* trigonometry) deals primarily with *right* triangles.

5. A right triangle is one containing a right (90°) angle.

6. The sum of the angles in a plane triangle is 180°; therefore, in a right triangle, the sum of the two angles other than the right angle is 90°.

7. The side opposite the right angle, in a right triangle, is known as the hypotenuse.

8. There is a relationship between the sides and angles of a right triangle such that as the lengths of the sides vary, the sizes of the angles (other than the right angle, of course) also vary. Or, conversely, as the size of the angles vary, the lengths of the sides vary.

9. Because of the relationship just referred to, we can say that the size of an angle (in a right triangle) depends upon the *ratio* existing between any two sides of the triangle.

Continue on the next page.

10. The ratio between two sides is simply the fraction we get when we indicate the division of the length of one side by the length of another. If we actually perform the indicated division, the resultant quotient is known as a "decimal" fraction.

11. Stated simply, it is the relationship between these ratios (representing the lengths of the sides) and the two variable angles that enables us to solve problems in trigonometry.

12. Because the ratios are so important, they are given names as follows:

$$\text{sine} = \frac{\text{opposite side}}{\text{hypotenuse}} \qquad \text{cosecant} = \frac{\text{hypotenuse}}{\text{opposite side}}$$

$$\text{cosine} = \frac{\text{adjacent side}}{\text{hypotenuse}} \qquad \text{secant} = \frac{\text{hypotenuse}}{\text{adjacent side}}$$

$$\text{tangent} = \frac{\text{opposite side}}{\text{adjacent side}} \qquad \text{cotangent} = \frac{\text{adjacent side}}{\text{opposite side}}$$

13. The ratios named above are known as the six "trigonometric functions" and usually are abbreviated as follows:

sin = sine	csc = cosecant
cos = cosine	sec = secant
tan = tangent	cot = cotangent

14. Referring to the triangle shown, whose sides and angles are identified in a conventional way, the six trigonometric functions can be expressed mathematically in terms of angle A' as follows:

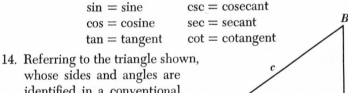

$$\sin A = \frac{a}{c} \qquad \csc A = \frac{c}{a}$$

$$\cos A = \frac{b}{c} \qquad \sec A = \frac{c}{b}$$

$$\tan A = \frac{a}{b} \qquad \cot A = \frac{b}{a}$$

Turn to the next page.

15. Note from item 14 that the csc, sec, and cot are, respectively, reciprocals of the sin, cos, and tan functions.

16. To find the missing parts (that is, the unknown values of sides and angles) of a right triangle, we use a trigonometric function (one of the six named above in items 12 and 14) that includes the *two known parts* of the triangle and *one of the unknown parts* we are trying to find.

17. Having selected the most suitable function, we first "solve" for the unknown part; that is, we transpose the equation (function) in such a way that the symbol for the unknown value is on the left-hand side of the equal sign, and the symbols for the known parts are on the right.

18. The third step in solving the problem is to substitute any known values in place of their respective symbols in the equation and perform the indicated multiplication or division to find the answer.

19. If the unknown quantity is an angle, the final step will be to find its value in the trigonometric tables by entering in the proper function column with the decimal fraction found as a result of the third step taken in item 18 above.

20. Tables of natural trigonometric functions, such as that found in Appendix A, simply show the relationship between the trigonometric functions (tabulated in decimal fractions) and their corresponding angles.

Proceed to the next page.

21. Because the two acute angles in a right triangle add up to 90°, they are said to be "complementary." This results, in trigonometry, in the two angles being co-functions of one another. That is, the sine of angle A is the cosine of angle B; the tangent of angle B is the cotangent of angle A; and the secant of angle A (or B) is cosecant of angle B (or A).

22. This handy matter of co-functions makes it unnecessary to print trigonometric tables beyond 45°, since the sine 46°, for instance, is equal to the *co*sine of 44° (90° − 46°). This means that we find the sine of 46° opposite 44° in the cosine column! The printer, therefore, simply changes the name at the *bottom* of the column to read "sin," prints "46°" at the bottom of the page, and reverses the minute values to read *up,* instead of down, along the right-hand edge of the page. And so it is with the other functions, whose values beyond 45° are handled similarly.

This completes the course, and if you'd like to see how much you have learned, turn to page 74, where you'll find a self-administered quiz that will help you evaluate the results of your efforts.

Answers to the questions will be found on page 78.

If you can answer 45 questions correctly (i.e., earn 45 points) without reference to the study material, you can consider that you have passed the course with flying colors.

Self-quiz

Circle the Correct Answer or Fill In the Missing Information

1. Trigonometry is the branch of mathematics that deals with the relationships existing between the sides and angles of triangles.   True   False

2. Plane trigonometry concerns itself with the study of plane triangles.   True   False

3. A "plane" triangle is one whose sides are straight lines lying in _____ plane(s).   different   same

4. A plane, in the mathematical sense, is a ____-dimensional surface.   two   three

5. Plane trigonometry deals primarily with right triangles.   True   False

6. A right triangle is one containing a right angle.   True   False

7. A right angle is a ____-angle. $75°$ $90°$

8. The sum of the angles in a plane triangle is ____. $90°$ $180°$

9. The sum of the two "other" angles in a right triangle is ____. $90°$ $180°$

10. The hypotenuse of a right triangle is the side opposite the right angle.   True   False

11. The sides and angles of a right triangle are related in such a way that as the length of one side increases, the size of the angle opposite _____.   decreases   increases

12. For any given size of angle (in a right triangle, of course), the sides of the triangle are in a fixed ratio.   True   False

13. The ratio between two sides is simply the indicated division of the length of one side by t__ l__ o_ a_____.

14. If we actually *perform* the division referred to in question 13, the resulting quotient is called a _____ fraction.

15. The ratios between the sides of a right triangle are known in trigonometry as the _____ (how many?) t_____ f_____.

16. The names of the ratios referred to in question 15 are as follows (use only as many spaces as you need):

    _____   _____
    _____   _____
    _____   _____
    _____   _____
    _____   _____

17. Give below the abbreviations for each of the ratios named above.

    _____   _____
    _____   _____
    _____   _____
    _____   _____
    _____   _____

18. Referring to the triangle shown, express each of the six functions (ratios) mathematically in terms of angle A.

    __ $A =$ __   __ $A =$ __

    __ $A =$ __   __ $A =$ __

    __ $A =$ __   __ $A =$ __

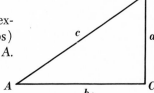

19. The three secondary functions are said to be r_____s of the three primary functions.

20. To solve for the unknown parts of a right triangle, we must know at least __(how many?) parts.

21. Tables of natural trigonometric functions supply the logarithms of the ratios between various pairs of sides of a right triangle.   True   False

22. Angles whose sum is 90° are known in mathematics as _____ angles.

    acute, obtuse,
       complementary

23. In a right triangle, the function of one angle is numerically equal to the co-function of the other angle.   True   False

24. (a) sin 24°55′ = _____

    (b) cos 36°18′ = _____

    (c) tan 65°01′ = _____

    (d) cot 84°43′ = _____

25. In the triangle shown, which function would you use to solve for:

    (*a*) Side *b*?
    (*b*) Side *c*? ———
    (*c*) Angle *A*? ———

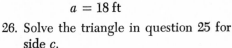

$$B = 49°22'$$
$$a = 18 \text{ ft}$$

26. Solve the triangle in question 25 for side *c*.
    Side *c* = ——————

27. Referring again to the triangle in question 25, what is the size of angle *A*?
    Angle *A* = ——————

28. What is the length of side *b*?
    Side *b* = ——————

Answers to Self-quiz

Give yourself one point for each answer, or *part* of an answer, you get right.

1. True
2. True
3. Same
4. two
5. True
6. True
7. 90°
8. 180°
9. 90°
10. True
11. increases
12. True
13. the length of another
14. decimal
15. six; trigonometric functions
16. sine, cosine, tangent, cosecant, secant, cotangent
17. sin, cos, tan, csc, sec, cot
18. $\sin A = \dfrac{a}{c}$, $\cos A = \dfrac{b}{c}$, $\tan A = \dfrac{a}{b}$, $\csc A = \dfrac{c}{a}$, $\sec A = \dfrac{c}{b}$, $\cot A = \dfrac{b}{a}$.
19. reciprocals
20. two

21. False
22. complementary
23. True
24. (a) 0.42130
    (b) 0.80593
    (c) 2.14610
    (d) 0.09247
25. (a) tan or cot
    (b) cos
    (c) none; simply subtract angle B from 90°
26. 27.6 ft
27. 40°38′
28. 21.0 ft

Glossary of Terms

Acute angle	An angle *less* than a right angle.
Acute triangle	One in which all angles are less than 90°.
Conversely	Turned about; acting oppositely.
Cosecant	Ratio of the hypotenuse to the opposite side; co-function of the secant.
Cosine	Ratio of the adjacent side to the hypotenuse; co-function of the sine.
Cotangent	Ratio of the adjacent side to the side opposite; co-function of the tangent.
Decimal fraction	A fraction stated in decimal form; the result of dividing a numerator by its denominator.
Denominator	The numbers (or symbols) below the line of a fraction.
Directly proportional	Increasing or decreasing in the *same* way as the referenced quantity.
Dividend	The number being divided.
Divisor	The number by which dividend is divided.
Equation	A statement that two expressions are equal.
Expression	A collection of terms combined by addition, subtraction, or both.

Fraction	Part of any object, quantity, or digit; usually indicated by two numbers—a numerator and denominator—separated by a fraction bar.
Function	A variable quantity that depends upon another quantity for its value; in the expression $y = 2x$, for example, y is said to be a function of x because its value will depend on, or vary with, the value(s) assigned to x.
Interpolation	The process of finding intermediate values (between those tabulated) through the use of proportional parts.
Inverse	Opposite in relation.
Inversely	Oppositely.
Inversely proportional	Increasing or decreasing *oppositely* to the referenced quantity.
Inverted	Turned upside down.
Numerator	The numbers (or symbols) above the line of a fraction.
Obtuse angle	An angle *greater* than a right angle.
Obtuse triangle	One that contains one angle greater than 90°.
Plane	Flat; two-dimensional.
Product	Result of multiplication.
Proportional	Changing correspondingly with some other quantity or term.
Quotient	Result of division.

Ratio	A relationship between two like numbers or like values (as, for instance, the lengths of two sides of a triangle).
Reciprocal	The inverted (upside down) version of a fraction.
Right angle	A 90° angle.
Right triangle	A triangle that contains one right angle.
Secant	Ratio of the hypotenuse to the adjacent side.
Sine	Ratio of the side opposite an angle to the hypotenuse.
Tangent	Ratio of the side opposite to the adjacent side.
Term (mathematical sense)	A combination of factors that are numbers or symbols combined by multiplication or division.
Transposition	Moving (transposing) terms across the equal sign.
Triangle (plane)	A geometric figure bounded by three straight lines.

Trigonometric functions (ratios)

Ratios of the sides of a right triangle as they relate to the size of the corresponding angles. Specifically,

Primary Functions

$$\text{sine} = \frac{\text{opposite side}}{\text{hypotenuse}}$$

$$\text{cosine} = \frac{\text{adjacent side}}{\text{hypotenuse}}$$

$$\text{tangent} = \frac{\text{opposite side}}{\text{adjacent side}}$$

Their Reciprocals

$$\text{cosecant} = \frac{\text{hypotenuse}}{\text{opposite side}}$$

$$\text{secant} = \frac{\text{hypotenuse}}{\text{adjacent side}}$$

$$\text{cotangent} = \frac{\text{adjacent side}}{\text{opposite side}}$$

Trigonometry

The branch of mathematics that deals with the measurement and solution of triangles.

Supplementary Problems

Solve using Appendix A, Tables of the Natural Trigonometric
Functions.   Answers will be found on page 88.

Given	Find (To nearest minute of arc and three significant figures)

1. $A = 30°18'$, $a = 3$ $B = $ ——, $c = $ ——, $b = $ ——

2. $a = 6$, $c = 11.8$ $A = $ ——, $B = $ ——, $b = $ ——

3. $a = 4$, $b = 3.9$ $A = $ ——, $B = $ ——, $c = $ ——

4. $A = 36°$, $c = 1$ $B = $ ——, $a = $ ——, $b = $ ——

5. $A = 75°32'$, $a = 80$ $B = $ ——, $b = $ ——, $c = $ ——

6. $A = 25°48'$, $a = 30$ $B = $ ——, $b = $ ——, $c = $ ——

7. $B = 15°19'$, $b = 20$ $A = $ ——, $a = $ ——, $c = $ ——

8. $a = 36.4$, $b = 100$ $A = $ ——, $B = $ ——, $c = $ ——

9. $B = 88°02'$, $b = .08$ $A = $ ——, $a = $ ——, $c = $ ——

10. $a = 30.2$, $c = 33.3$ $A = $ ——, $B = $ ——, $b = $ ——

Draw sketch for and solve each of the following problems.
(*Note:* If you need help on any of these, turn to page 86.)

11. Two battleships are stationed 3 miles apart.   From one an
enemy submarine is observed due south, and from the other
40°15′ east of south.   How far is the submarine from the
nearest battleship?

           Ans. ————

12. The vertical central pole of a circular tent is 20 feet high,
and its top is fastened by ropes 38 feet long to stakes set in
the ground.   How far are the stakes from the foot of the pole,
and what is the angle between the ropes and the ground?

           Ans. ————

13. At a distance of 58.6 feet from the base of a tower, the angle of elevation of its top is observed to be 58°24′. What is the height of the tower?

Ans. _____

14. If a tower casts a shadow which is three-fourths of its own length, what is the angle of elevation of the sun?

Ans. _____

15. From the top of a cliff 587 feet above sea level, the angles of depression (that is, angles below the horizontal) of two boats in line with the observer are 14°10′ and 24°45′, respectively. Find the distance between the boats.

Ans. _____

(Hints on next page.)

Hints on Supplementary Problems

11. Use the tangent function; see sketch.

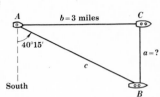

12. Use the sine function. Your sketch should look something like the one shown here.

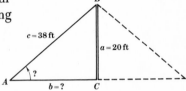

13. The tangent is called for. Check your sketch against the one shown here.

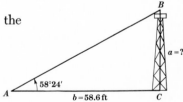

14. Again, the tangent is your function. Call the height of the tower 1, and the length of its shadow *three-fourths* (of 1, of course). See sketch.

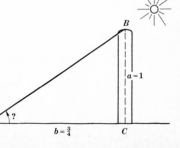

15. The sketch shown should help you get started right if you're having trouble with this problem. Recognize that you have *two* triangles to solve here (having the common side *a*) and that what you are seeking in each case is the length of the base (indicated by *b* and *b'* in the sketch). Once you have obtained these, you can then simply subtract the distance of the boat *nearest* the cliff from that of the boat *farthest* from shore to obtain the distance *between* the boats.

(Answers on next page.)

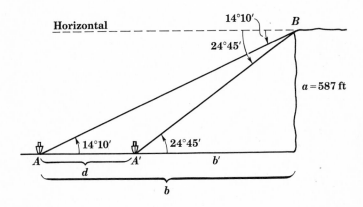

Answers to Supplementary Problems

1. $B = 59°42'$, $c = 5.95$, $b = 5.13$
2. $A = 30°34'$, $B = 59°26'$, $b = 10.2$
3. $A = 45°44'$, $B = 44°16'$, $c = 5.59$
4. $B = 54°00'$, $a = 0.588$, $b = 0.809$
5. $B = 14°28'$, $b = 20.6$, $c = 82.6$
6. $B = 64°12'$, $b = 62.1$, $c = 68.9$
7. $A = 74°41'$, $a = 73.0$, $c = 75.7$
8. $A = 20°00'$, $B = 70°00'$, $c = 106$
9. $A = 1°58'$, $a = 0.00275$, $c = 0.0802$
10. $A = 65°05'$, $B = 24°55'$, $b = 14.0$
11. 3.54 miles
12. $A = 31°45'$, $b = 32.3$ ft
13. 95.25 ft
14. $53°08'$
15. 1,050 ft

Note: If you accepted the invitation on page 65 to work these additional problems and have now completed them, you should return to page 49 and choose another alternative. Perhaps now you're ready to move on.

Appendix A

Natural Trigonometric Functions

(Correct to five significant figures)

′	sin	tan	cot	cos	
0	00000	.00000	∞	1.0000	60
1	029	029	3437.7	000	59
2	058	058	1718.9	000	58
3	087	087	1145.9	000	57
4	116	116	859.44	000	56
5	.00145	.00145	687.55	1.0000	55
6	175	175	572.96	000	54
7	204	204	491.11	000	53
8	233	233	429.72	000	52
9	262	262	381.97	000	51
10	.00291	.00291	343.77	1.0000	50
11	320	320	312.52	.99999	49
12	349	349	286.48	999	48
13	378	378	264.44	999	47
14	407	407	245.55	999	46
15	.00436	.00436	229.18	.99999	45
16	465	465	214.86	999	44
17	495	495	202.22	999	43
18	524	524	190.98	999	42
19	553	553	180.93	998	41
20	.00582	.00582	171.89	.99998	40
21	611	611	163.70	998	39
22	640	640	156.26	998	38
23	669	669	149.47	998	37
24	698	698	143.24	998	36
25	.00727	.00727	137.51	.99997	35
26	756	756	132.22	997	34
27	785	785	127.32	997	33
28	814	815	122.77	997	32
29	844	844	118.54	996	31
30	.00873	.00873	114.59	.99996	30
31	902	902	110.89	996	29
32	931	931	107.43	996	28
33	960	960	104.17	995	27
34	.00989	.00989	101.11	995	26
35	.01018	.01018	98.218	.99995	25
36	047	047	95.489	995	24
37	076	076	92.908	994	23
38	105	105	90.463	994	22
39	134	135	88.144	994	21
40	.01164	.01164	85.940	.99993	20
41	193	193	83.844	993	19
42	222	222	81.847	993	18
43	251	251	79.943	992	17
44	280	280	78.126	992	16
45	.01309	.01309	76.390	.99991	15
46	338	338	74.729	991	14
47	367	367	73.139	991	13
48	396	396	71.615	990	12
49	425	425	70.153	990	11
50	.01454	.01455	68.750	.99989	10
51	483	484	67.402	989	9
52	513	513	66.105	989	8
53	542	542	64.858	988	7
54	571	571	63.657	988	6
55	.01600	.01600	62.499	.99987	5
56	629	629	61.383	987	4
57	658	658	60.306	986	3
58	687	687	59.266	986	2
59	716	716	58.261	985	1
60	.01745	.01746	57.290	.99985	0
	cos	cot	tan	sin	′

89°

′	sin	tan	cot	cos	
0	.01745	.01746	57.290	.99985	60
1	774	775	56.351	984	59
2	803	804	55.442	984	58
3	832	833	54.561	983	57
4	862	862	53.709	983	56
5	.01891	.01891	52.882	.99982	55
6	920	920	52.081	982	54
7	949	949	51.303	981	53
8	.01978	.01978	50.549	980	52
9	.02007	.02007	49.816	980	51
10	.02036	.02036	49.104	.99979	50
11	065	066	48.412	979	49
12	094	095	47.740	978	48
13	123	124	47.085	977	47
14	152	153	46.449	977	46
15	.02181	.02182	45.829	.99976	45
16	211	211	45.226	976	44
17	240	240	44.639	975	43
18	269	269	44.066	974	42
19	298	298	43.508	974	41
20	.02327	.02328	42.964	.99973	40
21	356	357	42.433	972	39
22	385	386	41.916	972	38
23	414	415	41.411	971	37
24	443	444	40.917	970	36
25	.02472	.02473	40.436	.99969	35
26	501	502	39.965	969	34
27	530	531	39.506	968	33
28	560	560	39.057	967	32
29	589	589	38.618	966	31
30	.02618	.02619	38.188	.99966	30
31	647	648	37.769	965	29
32	676	677	37.358	964	28
33	705	706	36.956	963	27
34	734	735	36.563	963	26
35	.02763	.02764	36.178	.99962	25
36	792	793	35.801	961	24
37	821	822	35.431	960	23
38	850	851	35.070	959	22
39	879	881	34.715	959	2i
40	.02908	.02910	34.368	.99958	20
41	938	939	34.027	957	19
42	967	968	33.694	956	18
43	.02996	.02997	33.366	955	17
44	.03025	.03026	33.045	954	16
45	.03054	.03055	32.730	.99953	15
46	083	084	32.421	952	14
47	112	114	32.118	952	13
48	141	143	31.821	951	12
49	170	172	31.528	950	11
50	.03199	.03201	31.242	.99949	10
51	228	230	30.960	948	9
52	257	259	30.683	947	8
53	286	288	30.412	946	7
54	316	317	30.145	945	6
55	.03345	.03346	29.882	.99944	5
56	374	376	29.624	943	4
57	403	405	29.371	942	3
58	432	434	29.122	941	2
59	461	463	28.877	940	1
60	.03490	.03492	28.636	.99939	0
	cos	cot	tan	sin	′

88°

2°

′	sin	tan	cot	cos	
0	.03490	.03492	28.636	.99939	60
1	519	521	.399	938	59
2	548	550	28.166	937	58
3	577	579	27.937	936	57
4	606	609	.712	935	56
5	.03635	.03638	27.490	.99934	55
6	664	667	.271	933	54
7	693	696	27.057	932	53
8	723	725	26.845	931	52
9	752	754	.637	930	51
10	.03781	.03783	26.432	.99929	50
11	810	812	.230	927	49
12	839	842	26.031	926	48
13	868	871	25.835	925	47
14	897	900	.642	924	46
15	.03926	.03929	25.452	.99923	45
16	955	958	.264	922	44
17	.03984	.03987	25.080	921	43
18	.04013	.04016	24.898	919	42
19	042	046	.719	918	41
20	.04071	.04075	24.542	.99917	40
21	100	104	.368	916	39
22	129	133	.196	915	38
23	159	162	24.026	913	37
24	188	191	23.859	912	36
25	.04217	04220	23.695	.99911	35
26	246	250	.532	910	34
27	275	279	.372	909	33
28	304	308	.214	907	32
29	333	337	23.058	906	31
30	.04362	.04366	22.904	.99905	30
31	391	395	.752	904	29
32	420	424	.602	902	28
33	449	454	.454	901	27
34	478	483	.308	900	26
35	.04507	.04512	22.164	.99898	25
36	536	541	22.022	897	24
37	565	570	21.881	896	23
38	594	599	.743	894	22
39	623	628	.606	893	21
40	.04653	.04658	21.470	.99892	20
41	682	687	.337	890	19
42	711	716	.205	889	18
43	740	745	21.075	888	17
44	769	774	20.946	886	16
45	.04798	.04803	20.819	.99885	15
46	827	833	.693	883	14
47	856	862	.569	882	13
48	885	891	.446	881	12
49	914	920	.325	879	11
50	.04943	.04949	20.206	.99878	10
51	.04972	.04978	20.087	876	9
52	.05001	.05007	19.970	875	8
53	030	037	.855	873	7
54	059	066	.740	872	6
55	.05088	.05095	19.627	.99870	5
56	117	124	.516	869	4
57	146	153	.405	867	3
58	175	182	.296	866	2
59	205	212	.188	864	1
60	.05234	.05241	19.081	.99863	0
	cos	cot	tan	sin	′

87°

3°

′	sin	tan	cot	cos	
0	.05234	.05241	19.081	.99863	60
1	263	270	18.976	861	59
2	292	299	.871	860	58
3	321	328	.768	858	57
4	350	357	.666	857	56
5	.05379	.05387	18.564	.99855	55
6	408	416	.464	854	54
7	437	445	.366	852	53
8	466	474	.268	851	52
9	495	503	.171	849	51
10	.05524	.05533	18.075	.99847	50
11	553	562	17.980	846	49
12	582	591	.886	844	48
13	611	620	.793	842	47
14	640	649	.702	841	46
15	.05669	.05678	17.611	.99839	45
16	698	708	.521	838	44
17	727	737	.431	836	43
18	755	766	.343	834	42
19	785	795	.256	833	41
20	.05814	.05824	17.169	.99831	40
21	844	854	17.084	829	39
22	873	883	16.999	827	38
23	902	912	.915	826	37
24	931	941	.832	824	36
25	.05960	.05970	16.750	.99822	35
26	.05989	.05999	.668	821	34
27	.06018	.06029	.587	819	33
28	047	058	.507	817	32
29	076	087	.428	815	31
30	.06105	.06116	16.350	.99813	30
31	134	145	.272	812	29
32	163	175	.195	810	28
33	192	204	.119	808	27
34	221	233	16.043	806	26
35	.06250	.06262	15.969	.99804	25
36	279	291	.895	803	24
37	308	321	.821	801	23
38	337	350	.748	799	22
39	366	379	.676	797	21
40	.06395	.06408	15.605	.99795	20
41	424	438	.534	793	19
42	453	467	.464	792	18
43	482	496	.394	790	17
44	511	525	.325	788	16
45	.06540	.06554	15.257	.99786	15
46	569	584	.189	784	14
47	598	613	.122	782	13
48	627	642	15.056	780	12
49	656	671	14.990	778	11
50	.06685	.06700	14.924	.99776	10
51	714	730	.860	774	9
52	743	759	.795	772	8
53	773	788	.732	770	7
54	802	817	.669	768	6
55	.06831	.06847	14.606	.99766	5
56	860	876	.544	764	4
57	889	905	.482	762	3
58	918	934	.421	760	2
59	947	963	.361	758	1
60	.06976	.06993	14.301	.99756	0
	cos	cot	tan	sin	′

86°

4°

'	sin	tan	cot	cos	
0	06976	06993	14.301	99756	60
1	07005	07022	.241	754	59
2	034	051	.182	752	58
3	063	080	.124	750	57
4	092	110	.065	748	56
5	07121	07139	14.008	99746	55
6	150	168	13.951	744	54
7	179	197	.894	742	53
8	208	227	.838	740	52
9	237	256	.782	738	51
10	07266	07285	13.727	99736	50
11	295	314	.672	734	49
12	324	344	.617	731	48
13	353	373	.563	729	47
14	382	402	.510	727	46
15	07411	07431	13.457	99725	45
16	440	461	.404	723	44
17	469	490	.352	721	43
18	498	519	.300	719	42
19	527	548	.248	716	41
20	07556	07578	13.197	99714	40
21	585	607	.146	712	39
22	614	636	.096	710	38
23	643	665	13.046	708	37
24	672	695	12.996	705	36
25	07701	07724	12.947	99703	35
26	730	753	.898	701	34
27	759	782	.850	699	33
28	788	812	.801	696	32
29	817	841	.754	694	31
30	07846	07870	12.706	99692	30
31	875	899	.659	689	29
32	904	929	.612	687	28
33	933	958	.566	685	27
34	962	07987	.520	683	26
35	07991	08017	12.474	99680	25
36	08020	046	.429	678	24
37	049	075	.384	676	23
38	078	104	.339	673	22
39	107	134	.295	671	21
40	08136	08163	12.251	99668	20
41	165	192	.207	666	19
42	194	221	.163	664	18
43	223	251	.120	661	17
44	252	280	.077	659	16
45	08281	08309	12.035	99657	15
46	310	339	11.992	654	14
47	339	368	.950	652	13
48	368	397	.909	649	12
49	397	427	.867	647	11
50	08426	08456	11.826	99644	10
51	455	485	.785	642	9
52	484	514	.745	639	8
53	513	544	.705	637	7
54	542	573	.664	635	6
55	08571	08602	11.625	99632	5
56	600	632	.585	630	4
57	629	661	.546	627	3
58	658	690	.507	625	2
59	687	720	.468	622	1
60	08716	08749	11.430	99619	0
	cos	cot	tan	sin	'

85°

5°

'	sin	tan	cot	cos	
0	08716	08749	11.430	99619	60
1	745	778	.392	617	59
2	774	807	.354	614	58
3	803	837	.316	612	57
4	831	866	.279	609	56
5	08860	08895	11.242	99607	55
6	889	925	.205	604	54
7	918	954	.168	602	53
8	947	08983	.132	599	52
9	08976	09013	.095	596	51
10	09005	09042	11.059	99594	50
11	034	071	11.024	591	49
12	063	101	10.988	588	48
13	092	130	.953	586	47
14	121	159	.918	583	46
15	09150	09189	10.883	99580	45
16	179	218	.848	578	44
17	208	247	.814	575	43
18	237	277	.780	572	42
19	266	306	.746	570	41
20	09295	09335	10.712	99567	40
21	324	365	.678	564	39
22	353	394	.645	562	38
23	382	423	.612	559	37
24	411	453	.579	556	36
25	09440	09482	10.546	99553	35
26	469	511	.514	551	34
27	498	541	.481	548	33
28	527	570	.449	545	32
29	556	600	.417	542	31
30	09585	09629	10.385	99540	30
31	614	658	.354	537	29
32	642	688	.322	534	28
33	671	717	.291	531	27
34	700	746	.260	528	26
35	09729	09776	10.229	99526	25
36	758	805	.199	523	24
37	787	834	.168	520	23
38	816	864	.138	517	22
39	845	893	.108	514	21
40	09874	09923	10.078	99511	20
41	903	952	.048	508	19
42	932	09981	10.019	506	18
43	961	10011	9.9893	503	17
44	09990	040	.9601	500	16
45	10019	10069	9.9310	99497	15
46	048	099	.9021	494	14
47	077	128	.8734	491	13
48	106	158	.8448	488	12
49	135	187	.8164	485	11
50	10164	10216	9.7882	99482	10
51	192	246	.7601	479	9
52	221	275	.7322	476	8
53	250	305	.7044	473	7
54	279	334	.6768	470	6
55	10308	10363	9.6493	99467	5
56	337	393	.6220	464	4
57	366	422	.5949	461	3
58	395	452	.5679	458	2
59	424	481	.5411	455	1
60	10453	10510	9.5144	99452	0
	cos	cot	tan	sin	'

84°

6°

′	sin	tan	cot	cos	
0	.10453	.10510	9.5144	.99452	60
1	482	540	.4878	449	59
2	511	569	.4614	446	58
3	540	599	.4352	443	57
4	569	628	.4090	440	56
5	.10597	.10657	9.3831	.99437	55
6	626	687	.3572	434	54
7	655	716	.3315	431	53
8	684	746	.3060	428	52
9	713	775	.2806	424	51
10	.10742	.10805	9.2553	.99421	50
11	771	834	.2302	418	49
12	800	863	.2052	415	48
13	829	893	.1803	412	47
14	858	922	.1555	409	46
15	.10887	.10952	9.1309	.99406	45
16	916	.10981	.1065	402	44
17	945	.11011	.0821	399	43
18	.10973	040	.0579	396	42
19	.11002	070	.0338	393	41
20	.11031	.11099	9.0098	.99390	40
21	060	128	8.9860	386	39
22	089	158	.9623	383	38
23	118	187	.9387	380	37
24	147	217	.9152	377	36
25	.11176	.11246	8.8919	.99374	35
26	205	276	.8686	370	34
27	234	305	.8455	367	33
28	263	335	.8225	364	32
29	291	364	.7996	360	31
30	.11320	.11394	8.7769	.99357	30
31	349	423	.7542	354	29
32	378	452	.7317	351	28
33	407	482	.7093	347	27
34	436	511	.6870	344	26
35	.11465	.11541	8.6648	.99341	25
36	494	570	.6427	337	24
37	523	600	.6208	334	23
38	552	629	.5989	331	22
39	580	659	.5772	327	21
40	.11609	.11688	8.5555	.99324	20
41	638	718	.5340	320	19
42	667	747	.5126	317	18
43	696	777	.4913	314	17
44	725	806	.4701	310	16
45	.11754	.11836	8.4490	.99307	15
46	783	865	.4280	303	14
47	812	895	.4071	300	13
48	840	924	.3863	297	12
49	869	954	.3656	293	11
50	.11898	.11983	8.3450	.99290	10
51	927	.12013	.3245	286	9
52	956	042	.3041	283	8
53	.11985	072	.2838	279	7
54	.12014	101	.2636	276	6
55	.12043	.12131	8.2434	.99272	5
56	071	160	.2234	269	4
57	100	190	.2035	265	3
58	129	219	.1837	262	2
59	158	249	.1640	258	1
60	.12187	.12278	8.1443	.99255	0

| | cos | cot | tan | sin | ′ |

83°

7°

′	sin	tan	cot	cos	
0	.12187	.12278	8.1443	.99255	60
1	216	308	.1248	251	59
2	245	338	.1054	248	58
3	274	367	.0860	244	57
4	302	397	.0667	240	56
5	.12331	.12426	8.0476	.99237	55
6	360	456	.0285	233	54
7	389	485	8.0095	230	53
8	418	515	7.9906	226	52
9	447	544	.9718	222	51
10	.12476	.12574	7.9530	.99219	50
11	504	603	.9344	215	49
12	533	633	.9158	211	48
13	562	662	.8973	208	47
14	591	692	.8789	204	46
15	.12620	.12722	7.8606	.99200	45
16	649	751	8424	197	44
17	678	781	.8243	193	43
18	706	810	.8062	189	42
19	735	840	.7882	186	41
20	.12764	.12869	7.7704	.99182	40
21	793	899	.7525	178	39
22	822	929	.7348	175	38
23	851	958	.7171	171	37
24	880	.12988	.6996	167	36
25	.12908	.13017	7.6821	.99163	35
26	937	047	.6647	160	34
27	966	076	.6473	156	33
28	.12995	106	.6301	152	32
29	.13024	136	.6129	148	31
30	.13053	.13165	7.5958	.99144	30
31	081	195	.5787	141	29
32	110	224	.5618	137	28
33	139	254	.5449	133	27
34	168	284	.5281	129	26
35	.13197	.13313	7.5113	.99125	25
36	226	343	.4947	122	24
37	254	372	.4781	118	23
38	283	402	.4615	114	22
39	312	432	.4451	110	21
40	.13341	.13461	7.4287	.99106	20
41	370	491	.4124	102	19
42	399	521	.3962	098	18
43	427	550	.3800	094	17
44	456	580	.3639	091	16
45	.13485	.13609	7.3479	.99087	15
46	514	639	.3319	083	14
47	543	669	.3160	079	13
48	572	698	.3002	075	12
49	600	728	.2844	071	11
50	.13629	.13758	7.2687	.99067	10
51	658	787	.2531	063	9
52	687	817	.2375	059	8
53	716	846	.2220	055	7
54	744	876	.2066	051	6
55	.13773	.13906	7.1912	.99047	5
56	802	935	.1759	043	4
57	831	965	.1607	039	3
58	860	.13995	.1455	035	2
59	889	.14024	.1304	031	1
60	.13917	.14054	7.1154	.99027	0

| | cos | cot | tan | sin | ′ |

82°

′	sin	tan	cot	cos	
0	.13917	.14054	7.1154	.99027	60
1	946	084	.1004	023	59
2	.13975	113	.0855	019	58
3	.14004	143	.0706	015	57
4	033	173	.0558	011	56
5	.14061	.14202	7.0410	.99006	55
6	090	232	.0264	.99002	54
7	119	262	7.0117	.98998	53
8	148	291	6.9972	994	52
9	177	321	.9827	990	51
10	.14205	.14351	6.9682	.98986	50
11	234	381	.9538	982	49
12	263	410	.9395	978	48
13	292	440	.9252	973	47
14	320	470	.9110	969	46
15	.14349	.14499	6.8969	.98965	45
16	378	529	.8828	961	44
17	407	559	.8687	957	43
18	436	588	.8548	953	42
19	464	618	.8408	948	41
20	.14493	.14648	6.8269	.98944	40
21	522	678	.8131	940	39
22	551	707	.7994	936	38
23	580	737	.7856	931	37
24	608	767	.7720	927	36
25	.14637	.14796	6.7584	.98923	35
26	666	826	.7448	919	34
27	695	856	.7313	914	33
28	723	886	.7179	910	32
29	752	915	.7045	906	31
30	.14781	.14945	6.6912	.98902	30
31	810	.14975	.6779	897	29
32	838	.15005	.6646	893	28
33	867	034	.6514	889	27
34	896	064	.6383	884	26
35	.14925	.15094	6.6252	.98880	25
36	954	124	.6122	876	24
37	.14982	153	.5992	871	23
38	.15011	183	.5863	867	22
39	040	213	.5734	863	21
40	.15069	.15243	6.5606	.98858	20
41	097	272	.5478	854	19
42	126	302	.5350	849	18
43	155	332	.5223	845	17
44	184	362	.5097	841	16
45	.15212	.15391	6.4971	.98836	15
46	241	421	.4846	832	14
47	270	451	.4721	827	13
48	299	481	.4596	823	12
49	327	511	.4472	818	11
50	.15356	.15540	6.4348	.98814	10
51	385	570	.4225	809	9
52	414	600	.4103	805	8
53	442	630	.3980	800	7
54	471	660	.3859	796	6
55	.15500	.15689	6.3737	.98791	5
56	529	719	.3617	787	4
57	557	749	.3496	782	3
58	586	779	.3376	778	2
59	615	809	.3257	773	1
60	.15643	.15838	6.3138	.98769	0
	cos	cot	tan	sin	′

′	sin	tan	cot	cos	
0	.15643	.15838	6.3138	.98769	60
1	672	868	.3019	764	59
2	701	898	.2901	760	58
3	730	928	.2783	755	57
4	758	958	.2666	751	56
5	.15787	.15988	6.2549	.98746	55
6	816	.16017	.2432	741	54
7	845	047	.2316	737	53
8	873	077	.2200	732	52
9	902	107	.2085	728	51
10	.15931	.16137	6.1970	.98723	50
11	959	167	.1856	718	49
12	.15988	196	.1742	714	48
13	.16017	226	.1628	709	47
14	046	256	.1515	704	46
15	.16074	.16286	6.1402	.98700	45
16	103	316	.1290	695	44
17	132	346	.1178	690	43
18	160	376	.1066	686	42
19	189	405	.0955	681	41
20	.16218	.16435	6.0844	.98676	40
21	246	465	.0734	671	39
22	275	495	.0624	667	38
23	304	525	.0514	662	37
24	333	555	.0405	657	36
25	.16361	.16585	6.0296	.98652	35
26	390	615	.0188	648	34
27	419	645	6.0080	643	33
28	447	674	5.9972	638	32
29	476	704	.9865	633	31
30	.16505	.16734	5.9758	.98629	30
31	533	764	.9651	624	29
32	562	794	.9545	619	28
33	591	824	.9439	614	27
34	620	854	.9333	609	26
35	.16648	.16884	5.9228	.98604	25
36	677	914	.9124	600	24
37	706	944	.9019	595	23
38	734	.16974	.8915	590	22
39	763	.17004	.8811	585	21
40	.16792	.17033	5.8708	.98580	20
41	820	063	.8605	575	19
42	849	093	.8502	570	18
43	878	123	.8400	565	17
44	906	153	.8298	561	16
45	.16935	.17183	5.8197	.98556	15
46	964	213	.8095	551	14
47	16992	243	.7994	546	13
48	.17021	273	.7894	541	12
49	050	303	.7794	536	11
50	.17078	.17333	5.7694	.98531	10
51	107	363	.7594	526	9
52	136	393	.7495	521	8
53	164	423	.7396	516	7
54	193	453	.7297	511	6
55	.17222	.17483	5.7199	.98506	5
56	250	513	.7101	501	4
57	279	543	.7004	496	3
58	308	573	.6906	491	2
59	336	603	.6809	486	1
60	.17365	.17633	5.6713	.98481	0
	cos	cot	tan	sin	′

′	sin	tan	cot	cos	
0	.17365	.17633	5.6713	.98481	60
1	393	663	.6617	476	59
2	422	693	.6521	471	58
3	451	723	.6425	466	57
4	479	753	.6329	461	56
5	.17508	.17783	5.6234	.98455	55
6	537	813	.6140	450	54
7	565	843	.6045	445	53
8	594	873	.5951	440	52
9	623	903	.5857	435	51
10	.17651	.17933	5.5764	.98430	50
11	680	963	.5671	425	49
12	708	.17993	.5578	420	48
13	737	.18023	.5485	414	47
14	766	053	.5393	409	46
15	.17794	.18083	5.5301	.98404	45
16	823	113	.5209	399	44
17	852	143	.5118	394	43
18	880	173	.5026	389	42
19	909	203	.4936	383	41
20	.17937	.18233	5.4845	.98378	40
21	966	263	.4755	373	39
22	.17995	293	.4665	368	38
23	.18023	323	.4575	362	37
24	052	353	.4486	357	36
25	.18081	.18384	5.4397	.98352	35
26	109	414	.4308	347	34
27	138	444	.4219	341	33
28	166	474	.4131	336	32
29	195	504	.4043	331	31
30	.18224	.18534	5.3955	.98325	30
31	252	564	.3868	320	29
32	281	594	.3781	315	28
33	309	624	.3694	310	27
34	338	654	.3607	304	26
35	.18367	.18684	5.3521	.98299	25
36	395	714	.3435	294	24
37	424	745	.3349	288	23
38	452	775	.3263	283	22
39	481	805	.3178	277	21
40	.18509	.18835	5.3093	.98272	20
41	538	865	.3008	267	19
42	567	895	.2924	261	18
43	595	925	.2839	256	17
44	624	955	.2755	250	16
45	.18652	.18986	5.2672	.98245	15
46	681	.19016	.2588	240	14
47	710	046	.2505	234	13
48	738	076	.2422	229	12
49	767	106	.2339	223	11
50	.18795	.19136	5.2257	.98218	10
51	824	166	.2174	212	9
52	852	197	.2092	207	8
53	881	227	.2011	201	7
54	910	257	.1929	196	6
55	.18938	.19287	5.1848	.98190	5
56	967	317	.1767	185	4
57	.18995	347	.1686	179	3
58	.19024	378	.1606	174	2
59	052	408	.1526	168	1
60	.19081	.19438	5.1446	.98163	0
	cos	cot	tan	sin	′

′	sin	tan	cot	cos	
0	.19081	.19438	5.1446	.98163	60
1	109	468	.1366	157	59
2	138	498	.1286	152	58
3	167	529	.1207	146	57
4	195	559	.1128	140	56
5	.19224	.19589	5.1049	.98135	55
6	252	619	.0970	129	54
7	281	649	.0892	124	53
8	309	680	.0814	118	52
9	338	710	.0736	112	51
10	.19366	.19740	5.0658	.98107	50
11	395	770	.0581	101	49
12	423	801	.0504	096	48
13	452	831	.0427	090	47
14	481	861	.0350	084	46
15	.19509	.19891	5.0273	.98079	45
16	538	921	.0197	073	44
17	566	952	.0121	067	43
18	595	.19982	5.0045	061	42
19	623	.20012	4.9969	056	41
20	.19652	.20042	4.9894	.98050	40
21	680	073	.9819	044	39
22	709	103	.9744	039	38
23	737	133	.9669	033	37
24	766	164	.9594	027	36
25	.19794	.20194	4.9520	.98021	35
26	823	224	.9446	016	34
27	851	254	.9372	010	33
28	880	285	.9298	.98004	32
29	908	315	.9225	.97998	31
30	.19937	.20345	4.9152	.97992	30
31	965	376	.9078	987	29
32	.19994	406	.9006	981	28
33	.20022	436	.8933	975	27
34	051	466	.8860	969	26
35	.20079	.20497	4.8788	.97963	25
36	108	527	.8716	958	24
37	136	557	.8644	952	23
38	165	588	.8573	946	22
39	193	618	.8501	940	21
40	.20222	.20648	4.8430	.97934	20
41	250	679	.8359	928	19
42	279	709	.8288	922	18
43	307	739	.8218	916	17
44	336	770	.8147	910	16
45	.20364	.20800	4.8077	.97905	15
46	393	830	.8007	899	14
47	421	861	.7937	893	13
48	450	891	.7867	887	12
49	478	921	.7798	881	11
50	.20507	.20952	4.7729	.97875	10
51	535	.20982	.7659	869	9
52	563	.21013	.7591	863	8
53	592	043	.7522	857	7
54	620	073	.7453	851	6
55	.20649	.21104	4.7385	.97845	5
56	677	134	.7317	839	4
57	706	164	.7249	833	3
58	734	195	.7181	827	2
59	763	225	.7114	821	1
60	.20791	.21256	4.7046	.97815	0
	cos	cot	tan	sin	′

'	sin	tan	cot	cos	
0	.20791	.21256	4.7046	.97815	60
1	820	286	.6979	809	59
2	848	316	.6912	803	58
3	877	347	.6845	797	57
4	905̄	377	.6779	791	56
5	.20933	.21408	4.6712	.97784	55
6	962	438	.6646	778	54
7	.20990	469	.6580	772	53
8	.21019	499	.6514	766	52
9	047	529	.6448	760	51
10	.21076	.21560	4.6382	.97754	50
11	104	590	.6317	748	49
12	132	621	.6252	742	48
13	161	651	.6187	735	47
14	189	682	.6122	729	46
15	.21218	.21712	4.6057	.97723	45
16	246	743	.5993	717	44
17	275̄	773	.5928	711	43
18	303	804	.5864	705̄	42
19	331	834	.5800	698	41
20	.21360	.21864	4.5736	.97692	40
21	388	895̄	.5673	686	39
22	417	925	.5609	680	38
23	445	956	.5546	673	37
24	474	.21986	.5483	667	36
25	.21502	.22017	4.5420	.97661	35
26	530	047	.5357	655̄	34
27	559	078	.5294	648	33
28	587	108	.5232	642	32
29	616	139	.5169	636	31
30	.21644	.22169	4.5107	.97630	30
31	672	200	.5045	623	29
32	701	231	.4983	617	28
33	729	261	.4922	611	27
34	758	292	.4860	604	26
35	.21786	.22322	4.4799	.97598	25
36	814	353	.4737	592	24
37	843	383	.4676	585	23
38	871	414	.4615	579	22
39	899	444	.4555̄	573	21
40	.21928	.22475̄	4.4494	.97566	20
41	956	505	.4434	560	19
42	.21985̄	536	.4373	553	18
43	.22013	567	.4313	547	17
44	041	597	.4253	541	16
45	.22070	.22628	4.4194	.97534	15
46	098	658	.4134	528	14
47	126	689	.4075̄	521	13
48	155̄	719	.4015̄	515̄	12
49	183	750	.3956	508	11
50	.22212	.22781	4.3897	.97502	10
51	240	811	.3838	496	9
52	268	842	.3779	489	8
53	297	872	.3721	483	7
54	325	903	.3662	476	6
55	.22353	.22934	4.3604	.97470	5
56	382	964	.3546	463	4
57	410	.22995̄	.3488	457	3
58	438	.23026	.3430	450	2
59	467	056	.3372	444	1
60	.22495	.23087	4.3315̄	.97437	0
	cos	cot	tan	sin	'

77°

'	sin	tan	cot	cos	
0	.22495	.23087	4.3315̄	.97437	60
1	523	117	.3257	430	59
2	552	148	.3200	424	58
3	580	179	.3143	417	57
4	608	209	.3086	411	56
5	.22637	.23240	4.3029	.97404	55
6	665	271	.2972	398	54
7	693	301	.2916	391	53
8	722	332	.2859	384	52
9	750	363	.2803	378	51
10	.22778	.23393	4.2747	.97371	50
11	807	424	.2691	365̄	49
12	835	455̄	.2635	358	48
13	863	485	.2580	351	47
14	892	516	.2524	345̄	46
15	.22920	.23547	4.2468	.97338	45
16	948	578	.2413	331	44
17	.22977	608	.2358	325̄	43
18	.23005̄	639	.2303	318	42
19	033	670	.2248	311	41
20	.23062	.23700	4.2193	.97304	40
21	090	731	.2139	298	39
22	118	762	.2084	291	38
23	146	793	.2030	284	37
24	175̄	823	.1976	278	36
25	.23203	.23854	4.1922	.97271	35
26	231	885̄	.1868	264	34
27	260	916	.1814	257	33
28	288	946	.1760	251	32
29	316	.23977	.1706	244	31
30	.23345̄	.24008	4.1653	.97237	30
31	373	039	.1600	230	29
32	401	069	.1547	223	28
33	429	100	.1493	217	27
34	458	131	.1441	210	26
35	.23486	.24162	4.1388	.97203	25
36	514	193	.1335	196	24
37	542	223	.1282	189	23
38	571	254	.1230	182	22
39	599	285̄	.1178	176	21
40	.23627	.24316	4.1126	.97169	20
41	656	347	.1074	162	19
42	684	377	.1022	155̄	18
43	712	408	.0970	148	17
44	740	439	.0918	141	16
45	.23769	.24470	4.0867	.97134	15
46	797	501	.0815	127	14
47	825	532	.0764	120	13
48	853	562	.0713	113	12
49	882	593	.0662	106	11
50	.23910	.24624	4.0611	.97100	10
51	938	655̄	.0560	093	9
52	966	686	.0509	086	8
53	.23995̄	717	.0459	079	7
54	.24023	747	.0408	072	6
55	.24051	.24778	4.0358	.97063̄	5
56	079	809	.0308	058	4
57	108	840	.0257	051	3
58	136	871	.0207	044	2
59	164	902	.0158	037	1
60	.24192	.24933	4.0108	.97030	0
	cos	cot	tan	sin	'

76°

'	sin	tan	cot	cos	
0	.24192	.24933	4.0108	.97030	60
1	220	964	.0058	023	59
2	249	.24995	4.0009	015	58
3	277	.25026	3.9959	008	57
4	305	056	.9910	.97001	56
5	.24333	.25087	3.9861	.96994	55
6	362	118	.9812	987	54
7	390	149	.9763	980	53
8	418	180	.9714	973	52
9	446	211	.9665	966	51
10	.24474	.25242	3.9617	.96959	50
11	503	273	.9568	952	49
12	531	304	.9520	945	48
13	559	335	.9471	937	47
14	587	366	.9423	930	46
15	.24615	.25397	3.9375	.96923	45
16	644	428	.9327	916	44
17	672	459	.9279	909	43
18	700	490	.9232	902	42
19	728	521	.9184	894	41
20	.24756	.25552	3.9136	.96887	40
21	784	583	.9089	880	39
22	813	614	.9042	873	38
23	841	645	.8995	866	37
24	869	676	.8947	858	36
25	.24897	.25707	3.8900	.96851	35
26	925	738	.8854	844	34
27	954	769	.8807	837	33
28	.24982	800	.8760	829	32
29	.25010	831	.8714	822	31
30	.25038	.25862	3.8667	.96815	30
31	066	893	.8621	807	29
32	094	924	.8575	800	28
33	122	955	.8528	793	27
34	151	.25986	.8482	786	26
35	.25179	.26017	3.8436	.96778	25
36	207	048	.8391	771	24
37	235	079	.8345	764	23
38	263	110	.8299	756	22
39	291	141	.8254	749	21
40	.25320	.26172	3.8208	.96742	20
41	348	203	.8163	734	19
42	376	235	.8118	727	18
43	404	266	.8073	719	17
44	432	297	.8028	712	16
45	.25460	.26328	3.7983	.96705	15
46	488	359	.7938	697	14
47	516	390	.7893	690	13
48	545	421	.7848	682	12
49	573	452	.7804	675	11
50	.25601	.26483	3.7760	.96667	10
51	629	515	.7715	660	9
52	657	546	.7671	653	8
53	685	577	.7627	645	7
54	713	608	.7583	638	6
55	.25741	.26639	3.7539	.96630	5
56	769	670	.7495	623	4
57	798	701	.7451	615	3
58	826	733	.7408	608	2
59	854	764	.7364	600	1
60	.25882	.26795	3.7321	.96593	0

'	sin	tan	cot	cos	
0	.25882	.26795	3.7321	.96593	60
1	910	826	.7277	585	59
2	938	857	.7234	578	58
3	966	888	.7191	570	57
4	.25994	920	.7148	562	56
5	.26022	.26951	3.7105	.96555	55
6	050	.26982	.7062	547	54
7	079	.27013	.7019	540	53
8	107	044	.6976	532	52
9	135	076	.6933	524	51
10	.26163	.27107	3.6891	.96517	50
11	191	138	.6848	509	49
12	219	169	.6806	502	48
13	247	201	.6764	494	47
14	275	232	.6722	486	46
15	.26303	.27263	3.6680	.96479	45
16	331	294	.6638	471	44
17	359	326	.6596	463	43
18	387	357	.6554	456	42
19	415	388	.6512	448	41
20	.26443	.27419	3.6470	.96440	40
21	471	451	.6429	433	39
22	500	482	.6387	425	38
23	528	513	.6346	417	37
24	556	545	.6305	410	36
25	.26584	.27576	3.6264	.96402	35
26	612	607	.6222	394	34
27	640	638	.6181	386	33
28	668	670	.6140	379	32
29	696	701	.6100	371	31
30	.26724	.27732	3.6059	.96363	30
31	752	764	.6018	355	29
32	780	795	.5978	347	28
33	808	826	.5937	340	27
34	836	858	.5897	332	26
35	.26864	.27889	3.5856	.96324	25
36	892	921	.5816	316	24
37	920	952	.5776	308	23
38	948	.27983	.5736	301	22
39	.26976	.28015	.5696	293	21
40	.27004	.28046	3.5656	.96285	20
41	032	077	.5616	277	19
42	060	109	.5576	269	18
43	088	140	.5536	261	17
44	116	172	.5497	253	16
45	.27144	.28203	3.5457	.96246	15
46	172	234	.5418	238	14
47	200	266	.5379	230	13
48	228	297	.5339	222	12
49	256	329	.5300	214	11
50	.27284	.28360	3.5261	.96206	10
51	312	391	.5222	198	9
52	340	423	.5183	190	8
53	368	454	.5144	182	7
54	396	486	.5105	174	6
55	.27424	.28517	3.5067	.96166	5
56	452	549	.5028	158	4
57	480	580	.4989	150	3
58	508	612	.4951	142	2
59	536	643	.4912	134	1
60	.27564	.28675	3.4874	.96126	0

	cos	cot	tan	sin	'

75°   **74°**

′	sin	tan	cot	cos	
0	.27564	.28675	3.4874	.96126	60
1	592	706	.4836	118	59
2	620	738	.4798	110	58
3	648	769	.4760	102	57
4	676	801	.4722	094	56
5	.27704	.28832	3.4684	.96086	55
6	731	864	.4646	078	54
7	759	895	.4608	070	53
8	787	927	.4570	062	52
9	815	958	.4533	054	51
10	.27843	.28990	3.4495	.96046	50
11	871	.29021	.4458	037	49
12	899	053	.4420	029	48
13	927	084	.4383	021	47
14	955	116	.4346	013	46
15	.27983	.29147	3.4308	.96005	45
16	.28011	179	.4271	.95997	44
17	039	210	.4234	989	43
18	067	242	.4197	981	42
19	095	274	.4160	972	41
20	.28123	.29305	3.4124	.95964	40
21	150	337	.4087	956	39
22	178	368	.4050	948	38
23	206	400	.4014	940	37
24	234	432	.3977	931	36
25	.28262	.29463	3.3941	.95923	35
26	290	495	.3904	915	34
27	318	526	.3868	907	33
28	346	558	.3832	898	32
29	374	590	.3796	890	31
30	.28402	.29621	3.3759	.95882	30
31	429	653	.3723	874	29
32	457	685	.3687	865	28
33	485	716	.3652	857	27
34	513	748	.3616	849	26
35	.28541	.29780	3.3580	.95841	25
36	569	811	.3544	832	24
37	597	843	.3509	824	23
38	625	875	.3473	816	22
39	652	906	.3438	807	21
40	.28680	.29938	3.3402	.95799	20
41	708	.29970	.3367	791	19
42	736	.30001	.3332	782	18
43	764	033	.3297	774	17
44	792	065	.3261	766	16
45	.28820	.30097	3.3226	.95757	15
46	847	128	.3191	749	14
47	875	160	.3156	740	13
48	903	192	.3122	732	12
49	931	224	.3087	724	11
50	.28959	.30255	3.3052	.95715	10
51	.28987	287	.3017	707	9
52	.29015	319	.2983	698	8
53	042	351	.2948	690	7
54	070	382	.2914	681	6
55	.29098	.30414	3.2879	.95673	5
56	126	446	.2845	664	4
57	154	478	.2811	656	3
58	182	509	.2777	647	2
59	209	541	.2743	639	1
60	.29237	.30573	3.2709	.95630	0
	cos	cot	tan	sin	′

73°

′	sin	tan	cot	cos	
0	.29237	.30573	3.2709	.95630	60
1	265	605	.2675	622	59
2	293	637	.2641	613	58
3	321	669	.2607	605	57
4	348	700	.2573	596	56
5	.29376	.30732	3.2539	.95588	55
6	404	764	.2506	579	54
7	432	796	.2472	571	53
8	460	828	.2438	562	52
9	487	860	.2405	554	51
10	.29515	.30891	3.2371	.95545	50
11	543	923	.2338	536	49
12	571	955	.2305	528	48
13	599	.30987	.2272	519	47
14	626	.31019	.2238	511	46
15	.29654	.31051	3.2205	.95502	45
16	682	083	.2172	493	44
17	710	115	.2139	485	43
18	737	147	.2106	476	42
19	765	178	.2073	467	41
20	.29793	.31210	3.2041	.95459	40
21	821	242	.2008	450	39
22	849	274	.1975	441	38
23	876	306	.1943	433	37
24	904	338	.1910	424	36
25	.29932	.31370	3.1878	.95415	35
26	960	402	.1845	407	34
27	.29987	434	.1813	398	33
28	.30015	466	.1780	389	32
29	043	498	.1748	380	31
30	.30071	.31530	3.1716	.95372	30
31	098	562	.1684	363	29
32	126	594	.1652	354	28
33	154	626	.1620	345	27
34	182	658	.1588	337	26
35	.30209	.31690	3.1556	.95328	25
36	237	722	.1524	319	24
37	265	754	.1492	310	23
38	292	786	.1460	301	22
39	320	818	.1429	293	21
40	.30348	.31850	3.1397	.95284	20
41	376	882	.1366	275	19
42	403	914	.1334	266	18
43	431	946	.1303	257	17
44	459	.31978	.1271	248	16
45	.30486	.32010	3.1240	.95240	15
46	514	042	.1209	231	14
47	542	074	.1178	222	13
48	570	106	.1146	213	12
49	597	139	.1115	204	11
50	.30625	.32171	3.1084	.95195	10
51	653	203	.1053	186	9
52	680	235	.1022	177	8
53	708	267	.0991	168	7
54	736	299	.0961	159	6
55	.30763	.32331	3.0930	.95150	5
56	791	363	.0899	142	4
57	819	396	.0868	133	3
58	846	428	.0838	124	2
59	874	460	.0807	115	1
60	.30902	.32492	3.0777	.95106	0
	cos	cot	tan	sin	′

72°

	sin	tan	cot	cos			sin	tan	cot	cos	
0	.30902	.32492	3.0777	.95106	60	0	.32557	.34433	2.9042	.94552	60
1	929	524	.0746	097	59	1	584	465	.9015	542	59
2	957	556	.0716	088	58	2	612	498	.8987	533	58
3	.30985	588	.0686	079	57	3	639	530	.8960	523	57
4	.31012	621	.0655	070	56	4	667	563	.8933	514	56
5	.31040	.32653	3.0625	.95061	55	5	.32694	.34596	2.8905	.94504	55
6	068	685	.0595	052	54	6	722	628	.8878	495	54
7	095	717	.0565	043	53	7	749	661	.8851	485	53
8	123	749	.0535	033	52	8	777	693	.8824	476	52
9	151	782	.0505	024	51	9	804	726	.8797	466	51
10	.31178	.32814	3.0475	.95015	50	10	.32832	.34758	2.8770	.94457	50
11	206	846	.0445	.95006	49	11	859	791	.8743	447	49
12	233	878	.0415	.94997	48	12	887	824	.8716	438	48
13	261	911	.0385	988	47	13	914	856	.8689	428	47
14	289	943	.0356	979	46	14	942	889	.8662	418	46
15	.31316	.32975	3.0326	.94970	45	15	.32969	.34922	2.8636	.94409	45
16	344	.33007	.0296	961	44	16	.32997	954	.8609	399	44
17	372	040	.0267	952	43	17	.33024	.34987	.8582	390	43
18	399	072	.0237	943	42	18	051	.35020	.8556	380	42
19	427	104	.0208	933	41	19	079	052	.8529	370	41
20	.31454	.33136	3.0178	.94924	40	20	.33106	.35085	2.8502	.94361	40
21	482	169	.0149	915	39	21	134	118	.8476	351	39
22	510	201	.0120	906	38	22	161	150	.8449	342	38
23	537	233	.0090	897	37	23	189	183	.8423	332	37
24	565	266	.0061	888	36	24	216	216	.8397	322	36
25	.31593	.33298	3.0032	.94878	35	25	.33244	.35248	2.8370	.94313	35
26	620	330	3.0003	869	34	26	271	281	.8344	303	34
27	648	363	2.9974	860	33	27	298	314	.8318	293	33
28	675	395	.9945	851	32	28	326	346	.8291	284	32
29	703	427	.9916	842	31	29	353	379	.8265	274	31
30	.31730	.33460	2.9887	.94832	30	30	.33381	.35412	2.8239	.94264	30
31	758	492	.9858	823	29	31	408	445	.8213	254	29
32	786	524	.9829	814	28	32	436	477	.8187	245	28
33	813	557	.9800	805	27	33	463	510	.8161	235	27
34	841	589	.9772	795	26	34	490	543	.8135	225	26
35	.31868	.33621	2.9743	.94786	25	35	.33518	.35576	2.8109	.94215	25
36	896	654	.9714	777	24	36	545	608	.8083	206	24
37	923	686	.9686	768	23	37	573	641	.8057	196	23
38	951	718	.9657	758	22	38	600	674	.8032	186	22
39	.31979	751	.9629	749	21	39	627	707	.8006	176	21
40	.32006	33783	2.9600	.94740	20	40	.33655	.35740	2.7980	.94167	20
41	034	816	.9572	730	19	41	682	772	.7955	157	19
42	061	848	.9544	721	18	42	710	805	.7929	147	18
43	089	881	.9515	712	17	43	737	838	.7903	137	17
44	116	913	.9487	702	16	44	764	871	.7878	127	16
45	.32144	.33945	2.9459	.94693	15	45	.33792	.35904	2.7852	.94118	15
46	171	.33978	.9431	684	14	46	819	937	.7827	108	14
47	199	.34010	.9403	674	13	47	846	.35969	.7801	098	13
48	227	043	.9375	665	12	48	874	.36002	.7776	088	12
49	254	075	.9347	656	11	49	901	035	.7751	078	11
50	.32282	.34108	2.9319	.94646	10	50	.33929	.36068	2.7725	.94068	10
51	309	140	.9291	637	9	51	956	101	.7700	058	9
52	337	173	.9263	627	8	52	.33983	134	.7675	049	8
53	364	205	.9235	618	7	53	.34011	167	.7650	039	7
54	392	238	.9208	609	6	54	038	199	.7625	029	6
55	.32419	.34270	2.9180	.94599	5	55	.34065	.36232	2.7600	.94019	5
56	447	303	.9152	590	4	56	093	265	.7575	.94009	4
57	474	335	.9125	580	3	57	120	298	.7550	.93999	3
58	502	368	.9097	571	2	58	147	331	.7525	989	2
59	529	400	.9070	561	1	59	175	364	.7500	979	1
60	.32557	.34433	2.9042	.94552	0	60	.34202	.36397	2.7475	.93969	0
	cos	cot	tan	sin	'		cos	cot	tan	sin	'

′	sin	tan	cot	cos	
0	.34202	.36397	2.7475	.93969	60
1	229	430	.7450	959	59
2	257	463	.7425	949	58
3	284	496	.7400	939	57
4	311	529	.7376	929	56
5	.34339	.36562	2.7351	.93919	55
6	366	595	.7326	909	54
7	393	628	.7302	899	53
8	421	661	.7277	889	52
9	448	694	.7253	879	51
10	.34475	.36727	2.7228	.93869	50
11	503	760	.7204	859	49
12	530	793	.7179	849	48
13	557	826	.7155	839	47
14	584	859	.7130	829	46
15	.34612	.36892	2.7106	.93819	45
16	639	925	.7082	809	44
17	666	958	.7058	799	43
18	694	.36991	.7034	789	42
19	721	.37024	.7009	779	41
20	.34748	.37057	2.6985	.93769	40
21	775	090	.6961	759	39
22	803	123	.6937	748	38
23	830	157	.6913	738	37
24	857	190	.6889	728	36
25	.34884	.37223	2.6865	.93718	35
26	912	256	.6841	708	34
27	939	289	.6818	698	33
28	966	322	.6794	688	32
29	.34993	355	.6770	677	31
30	.35021	.37388	2.6746	.93667	30
31	048	422	.6723	657	29
32	075	455	.6699	647	28
33	102	488	.6675	637	27
34	130	521	.6652	626	26
35	.35157	.37554	2.6628	.93616	25
36	184	588	.6605	606	24
37	211	621	.6581	596	23
38	239	654	.6558	585	22
39	266	687	.6534	575	21
40	.35293	.37720	2.6511	.93565	20
41	320	754	.6488	555	19
42	347	787	.6464	544	18
43	375	820	.6441	534	17
44	402	853	.6418	524	16
45	.35429	.37887	2.6395	.93514	15
46	456	920	.6371	503	14
47	484	953	.6348	493	13
48	511	.37986	.6325	483	12
49	538	.38020	.6302	472	11
50	.35565	.38053	2.6279	.93462	10
51	592	086	.6256	452	9
52	619	120	.6233	441	8
53	647	153	.6210	431	7
54	674	186	.6187	420	6
55	.35701	.38220	2.6165	.93410	5
56	728	253	.6142	400	4
57	755	286	.6119	389	3
58	782	320	.6096	379	2
59	810	353	.6074	368	1
60	.35837	.38386	2.6051	.93358	0
	cos	cot	tan	sin	′

69°

′	sin	tan	cot	cos	
0	.35837	.38386	2.6051	.93358	60
1	864	420	.6028	348	59
2	891	453	.6006	337	58
3	918	487	.5983	327	57
4	945	520	.5961	316	56
5	.35973	.38553	2.5938	.93306	55
6	.36000	587	.5916	295	54
7	027	620	.5893	285	53
8	054	654	.5871	274	52
9	081	687	.5848	264	51
10	.36108	.38721	2.5826	.93253	50
11	135	754	.5804	243	49
12	162	787	.5782	232	48
13	190	821	.5759	222	47
14	217	854	.5737	211	46
15	.36244	.38888	2.5713	.93201	45
16	271	921	.5693	190	44
17	298	955	.5671	180	43
18	325	.38988	.5649	169	42
19	352	.39022	.5627	159	41
20	.36379	.39055	2.5605	.93148	40
21	406	089	.5583	137	39
22	434	122	.5561	127	38
23	461	156	.5539	116	37
24	488	190	.5517	106	36
25	.36515	.39223	2.5495	.93095	35
26	542	257	.5473	084	34
27	569	290	.5452	074	33
28	596	324	.5430	063	32
29	623	357	.5408	052	31
30	.36650	.39391	2.5386	.93042	30
31	677	425	.5365	031	29
32	704	458	.5343	020	28
33	731	492	.5322	.93010	27
34	758	526	.5300	.92999	26
35	.36785	.39559	2.5279	.92988	25
36	812	593	.5257	978	24
37	839	626	.5236	967	23
38	867	660	.5214	956	22
39	894	694	.5193	945	21
40	.36921	.39727	2.5172	.92935	20
41	948	761	.5150	924	19
42	.36975	795	.5129	913	18
43	.37002	829	.5108	902	17
44	029	862	.5086	892	16
45	.37056	.39896	2.5065	.92881	15
46	083	930	.5044	870	14
47	110	963	.5023	859	13
48	137	.39997	.5002	849	12
49	164	.40031	.4981	838	11
50	.37191	.40065	2.4960	.92827	10
51	218	098	.4939	816	9
52	245	132	.4918	805	8
53	272	166	.4897	794	7
54	299	200	.4876	784	6
55	.37326	.40234	2.4855	.92773	5
56	353	267	.4834	762	4
57	380	301	.4813	751	3
58	407	335	.4792	740	2
59	434	369	.4772	729	1
60	.37461	.40403	2.4751	.92718	0
	cos	cot	tan	sin	′

68°

′	sin	tan	cot	cos	
0	.37461	.40403	2.4751	.92718	60
1	488	436	.4730	707	59
2	515	470	.4709	697	58
3	542	504	.4689	686	57
4	569	538	.4668	675	56
5	.37595	.40572	2.4648	.92664	55
6	622	606	.4627	653	54
7	649	640	.4606	642	53
8	676	674	.4586	631	52
9	703	707	.4566	620	51
10	.37730	.40741	2.4545	.92609	50
11	757	775	.4525	598	49
12	784	809	.4504	587	48
13	811	843	.4484	576	47
14	838	877	.4464	565	46
15	.37865	.40911	2.4443	.92554	45
16	892	945	.4423	543	44
17	919	.40979	.4403	532	43
18	946	.41013	.4383	521	42
19	973	047	.4362	510	41
20	.37999	.41081	2.4342	.92499	40
21	.38026	115	.4322	488	39
22	053	149	.4302	477	38
23	080	183	.4282	466	37
24	107	217	.4262	455	36
25	.38134	.41251	2.4242	.92444	35
26	161	285	.4222	432	34
27	188	319	.4202	421	33
28	215	353	.4182	410	32
29	241	387	.4162	399	31
30	.38268	.41421	2.4142	.92388	30
31	295	455	.4122	377	29
32	322	490	.4102	366	28
33	349	524	.4083	355	27
34	376	558	.4063	343	26
35	.38403	.41592	2.4043	.92332	25
36	430	626	.4023	321	24
37	456	660	.4004	310	23
38	483	694	.3984	299	22
39	510	728	.3964	287	21
40	.38537	.41763	2.3945	.92276	20
41	564	797	.3925	265	19
42	591	831	.3906	254	18
43	617	865	.3886	243	17
44	644	899	.3867	231	16
45	.38671	.41933	2.3847	.92220	15
46	698	.41968	.3828	209	14
47	725	.42002	.3808	198	13
48	752	036	.3789	186	12
49	778	070	.3770	175	11
50	.38805	.42105	2.3750	.92164	10
51	832	139	.3731	152	9
52	859	173	.3712	141	8
53	886	207	.3693	130	7
54	912	242	.3673	119	6
55	.38939	.42276	2.3654	.92107	5
56	966	310	.3635	096	4
57	.38993	345	.3616	085	3
58	.39020	379	.3597	073	2
59	046	413	.3578	062	1
60	.39073	.42447	2.3559	.92050	0

| | cos | cot | tan | sin | ′ |

′	sin	tan	cot	cos	
0	.39073	.42447	2.3559	.92050	60
1	100	482	.3539	039	59
2	127	516	.3520	028	58
3	153	551	.3501	016	57
4	180	585	.3483	.92005	56
5	.39207	.42619	2.3464	.91994	55
6	234	654	.3445	982	54
7	260	688	.3426	971	53
8	287	722	.3407	959	52
9	314	757	.3388	948	51
10	.39341	.42791	2.3369	.91936	50
11	367	826	.3351	925	49
12	394	860	.3332	914	48
13	421	894	.3313	902	47
14	448	929	.3294	891	46
15	.39474	.42963	2.3276	.91879	45
16	501	.42998	.3257	868	44
17	528	.43032	.3238	856	43
18	555	067	.3220	845	42
19	581	101	.3201	833	41
20	.39608	.43136	2.3183	.91822	40
21	635	170	.3164	810	39
22	661	205	.3146	799	38
23	688	239	.3127	787	37
24	715	274	.3109	775	36
25	.39741	.43308	2.3090	.91764	35
26	768	343	.3072	752	34
27	795	378	.3053	741	33
28	822	412	.3035	729	32
29	848	447	.3017	718	31
30	.39875	.43481	2.2998	.91706	30
31	902	516	.2980	694	29
32	928	550	.2962	683	28
33	955	585	.2944	671	27
34	.39982	620	.2925	660	26
35	.40008	.43654	2.2907	.91648	25
36	035	689	.2889	636	24
37	062	724	.2871	625	23
38	088	758	.2853	613	22
39	115	793	.2835	601	21
40	.40141	.43828	2.2817	.91590	20
41	168	862	.2799	578	19
42	195	897	.2781	566	18
43	221	932	.2763	555	17
44	248	.43966	.2745	543	16
45	.40275	.44001	2.2727	.91531	15
46	301	036	.2709	519	14
47	328	071	.2691	508	13
48	355	105	.2673	496	12
49	381	140	.2655	484	11
50	.40408	.44175	2.2637	.91472	10
51	434	210	.2620	461	9
52	461	244	.2602	449	8
53	488	279	.2584	437	7
54	514	314	.2566	425	6
55	.40541	.44349	2.2549	.91414	5
56	567	384	.2531	402	4
57	594	418	.2513	390	3
58	621	453	.2496	378	2
59	647	488	.2478	366	1
60	.40674	.44523	2.2460	.91355	0

| | cos | cot | tan | sin | ′ |

′	sin	tan	cot	cos	
0	.40674	.44523	2.2460	.91355	60
1	700	558	.2443	343	59
2	727	593	.2425	331	58
3	753	627	.2408	319	57
4	780	662	.2390	307	56
5	.40806	.44697	2.2373	.91295	55
6	833	732	.2355	283	54
7	860	767	.2338	272	53
8	886	802	.2320	260	52
9	913	837	.2303	248	51
10	.40939	.44872	2.2286	.91236	50
11	966	907	.2268	224	49
12	.40992	942	.2251	212	48
13	.41019	.44977	.2234	200	47
14	045	.45012	.2216	188	46
15	.41072	.45047	2.2199	.91176	45
16	098	082	.2182	164	44
17	125	117	.2165	152	43
18	151	152	.2148	140	42
19	178	187	.2130	128	41
20	.41204	.45222	2.2113	.91116	40
21	231	257	.2096	104	39
22	257	292	.2079	092	38
23	284	327	.2062	080	37
24	310	362	.2045	068	36
25	.41337	.45397	2.2028	.91056	35
26	363	432	.2011	044	34
27	390	467	.1994	032	33
28	416	502	.1977	020	32
29	443	538	.1960	.91008	31
30	.41469	.45573	2.1943	.90996	30
31	496	608	.1926	984	29
32	522	643	.1909	972	28
33	549	678	.1892	960	27
34	575	713	.1876	948	26
35	.41602	.45748	2.1859	.90936	25
36	628	784	.1842	924	24
37	655	819	.1825	911	23
38	681	854	.1808	899	22
39	707	889	.1792	887	21
40	.41734	.45924	2.1775	.90875	20
41	760	960	.1758	863	19
42	787	.45995	.1742	851	18
43	813	.46030	.1725	839	17
44	840	065	.1708	826	16
45	.41866	.46101	2.1692	.90814	15
46	892	136	.1675	802	14
47	919	171	.1659	790	13
48	945	206	.1642	778	12
49	972	242	.1625	766	11
50	.41998	.46277	2.1609	.90753	10
51	.42024	312	.1592	741	9
52	051	348	.1576	729	8
53	077	383	.1560	717	7
54	104	418	.1543	704	6
55	.42130	.46454	2.1527	.90692	5
56	156	489	.1510	680	4
57	183	525	.1494	668	3
58	209	560	.1478	655	2
59	235	595	.1461	643	1
60	.42262	.46631	2.1445	.90631	0
	cos	cot	tan	sin	′

′	sin	tan	cot	cos	
0	.42262	.46631	2.1445	.90631	60
1	288	666	.1429	618	59
2	315	702	.1413	606	58
3	341	737	.1396	594	57
4	367	772	.1380	582	56
5	.42394	.46808	2.1364	.90569	55
6	420	843	.1348	557	54
7	446	879	.1332	545	53
8	473	914	.1315	532	52
9	499	950	.1299	520	51
10	.42525	.46985	2.1283	.90507	50
11	552	.47021	.1267	495	49
12	578	056	.1251	483	48
13	604	092	.1235	470	47
14	631	128	.1219	458	46
15	.42657	.47163	2.1203	.90446	45
16	683	199	.1187	433	44
17	709	234	.1171	421	43
18	736	270	.1155	408	42
19	762	305	.1139	396	41
20	.42788	.47341	2.1123	.90383	40
21	815	377	.1107	371	39
22	841	412	.1092	358	38
23	867	448	.1076	346	37
24	894	483	.1060	334	36
25	.42920	.47519	2.1044	.90321	35
26	946	555	.1028	309	34
27	972	590	.1013	296	33
28	.42999	626	0997	284	32
29	.43025	662	.0981	271	31
30	.43051	.47698	2.0965	.90259	30
31	077	733	.0950	246	29
32	104	769	.0934	233	28
33	130	805	.0918	221	27
34	156	840	.0903	208	26
35	.43182	.47876	2.0887	.90196	25
36	209	912	.0872	183	24
37	235	948	.0856	171	23
38	261	.47984	.0840	158	22
39	287	.48019	.0825	146	21
40	.43313	.48055	2.0809	.90133	20
41	340	091	.0794	120	19
42	366	127	.0778	108	18
43	392	163	.0763	095	17
44	418	198	.0748	083	16
45	.43445	.48234	2.0732	.90070	15
46	471	270	.0717	057	14
47	497	306	.0701	045	13
48	523	342	.0686	032	12
49	549	378	.0671	019	11
50	.43575	.48414	2.0655	.90007	10
51	602	450	.0640	.89994	9
52	628	486	.0625	981	8
53	654	521	.0609	968	7
54	680	557	.0594	956	6
55	.43706	.48593	2.0579	.89943	5
56	733	629	.0564	930	4
57	759	665	.0549	918	3
58	785	701	.0533	905	2
59	811	737	.0518	892	1
60	.43837	.48773	2.0503	.89879	0
	cos	cot	tan	sin	′

'	sin	tan	cot	cos	
0	.43837	.48773	2.0503	.89879	60
1	863	809	.0488	867	59
2	889	845	.0473	854	58
3	916	881	.0458	841	57
4	942	917	.0443	828	56
5	.43968	.48953	2.0428	.89816	55
6	.43994	.48989	.0413	803	54
7	.44020	.49026	.0398	790	53
8	046	062	.0383	777	52
9	072	098	.0368	764	51
10	.44098	.49134	2.0353	.89752	50
11	124	170	.0338	739	49
12	151	206	.0323	726	48
13	177	242	.0308	713	47
14	203	278	.0293	700	46
15	.44229	.49315	2.0278	.89687	45
16	255	351	.0263	674	44
17	281	387	.0248	662	43
18	307	423	.0233	649	42
19	333	459	.0219	636	41
20	.44359	.49495	2.0204	.89623	40
21	385	532	.0189	610	39
22	411	568	.0174	597	38
23	437	604	.0160	584	37
24	464	640	.0145	571	36
25	.44490	.49677	2.0130	.89558	35
26	516	713	.0115	545	34
27	542	749	.0101	532	33
28	568	786	.0086	519	32
29	594	822	.0072	506	31
30	.44620	.49858	2.0057	.89493	30
31	646	894	.0042	480	29
32	672	931	.0028	467	28
33	698	.49967	2.0013	454	27
34	724	.50004	1.9999	441	26
35	.44750	.50040	1.9984	.89428	25
36	776	076	.9970	415	24
37	802	113	.9955	402	23
38	828	149	.9941	389	22
39	854	185	.9926	376	21
40	.44880	.50222	1.9912	.89363	20
41	906	258	.9897	350	19
42	932	295	.9883	337	18
43	958	331	.9868	324	17
44	.44984	368	.9854	311	16
45	.45010	.50404	1.9840	.89298	15
46	036	441	.9825	285	14
47	062	477	.9811	272	13
48	088	514	.9797	259	12
49	114	550	.9782	245	11
50	.45140	.50587	1.9768	.89232	10
51	166	623	.9754	219	9
52	192	660	.9740	206	8
53	218	696	9725	193	7
54	243	733	.9711	180	6
55	.45269	.50769	1.9697	.89167	5
56	295	806	.9683	153	4
57	321	843	.9669	140	3
58	347	879	.9654	127	2
59	373	916	.9640	114	1
60	.45399	.50953	1.9626	.89101	0
	cos	cot	tan	sin	'

63°

'	sin	tan	cot	cos	
0	.45399	.50953	1.9626	.89101	60
1	425	.50989	.9612	087	59
2	451	.51026	.9598	074	58
3	477	063	.9584	061	57
4	503	.099	.9570	048	56
5	.45529	.51136	1.9556	.89035	55
6	554	173	.9542	021	54
7	580	209	.9528	.89008	53
8	606	246	.9514	.88995	52
9	632	283	.9500	981	51
10	.45658	.51319	1.9486	.88968	50
11	684	356	.9472	955	49
12	710	393	.9458	942	48
13	736	430	.9444	928	47
14	762	467	.9430	915	46
15	.45787	.51503	1.9416	.88902	45
16	813	540	.9402	888	44
17	839	577	.9388	875	43
18	865	614	.9375	862	42
19	891	651	.9361	848	41
20	.45917	.51688	1.9347	.88835	40
21	942	724	.9333	822	39
22	968	761	.9319	808	38
23	.45994	798	.9306	795	37
24	.46020	835	.9292	782	36
25	.46046	.51872	1.9278	.88768	35
26	072	909	.9265	755	34
27	097	946	.9251	741	33
28	123	.51983	.9237	728	32
29	149	.52020	.9223	715	31
30	.46175	.52057	1.9210	.88701	30
31	201	094	.9196	688	29
32	226	131	.9183	674	28
33	252	168	.9169	661	27
34	278	205	.9155	647	26
35	.46304	.52242	1.9142	.88634	25
36	330	279	.9128	620	24
37	355	316	.9115	607	23
38	381	353	.9101	593	22
39	407	390	.9088	580	21
40	.46433	.52427	1.9074	.88566	20
41	458	464	.9061	553	19
42	484	501	.9047	539	18
43	510	538	9034	526	17
44	536	575	.9020	512	16
45	.46561	.52613	1.9007	.88499	15
46	587	650	.8993	485	14
47	613	687	.8980	472	13
48	639	724	.8967	458	12
49	664	761	.8953	445	11
50	.46690	.52798	1.8940	.88431	10
51	716	836	.8927	417	9
52	742	873	.8913	404	8
53	767	910	.8900	390	7
54	793	947	.8887	377	6
55	.46819	.52985	1.8873	.88363	5
56	844	.53022	.8860	349	4
57	870	059	.8847	336	3
58	896	096	.8834	322	2
59	921	134	.8820	308	1
60	.46947	.53171	1.8807	.88295	0
	cos	cot	tan	sin	'

62°

28°

′	sin	tan	cot	cos	
0	.46947	.53171	1.8807	.88295	60
1	973	208	.8794	281	59
2	.46999	246	.8781	267	58
3	.47024	283	.8768	254	57
4	050	320	.8755	240	56
5	.47076	.53358	1.8741	.88226	55
6	101	395	.8728	213	54
7	127	432	.8715	199	53
8	153	470	.8702	185	52
9	178	507	.8689	172	51
10	.47204	.53545	1.8676	.88158	50
11	229	582	.8663	144	49
12	255	620	.8650	130	48
13	281	657	.8637	117	47
14	306	694	.8624	103	46
15	.47332	.53732	1.8611	.88089	45
16	358	769	.8598	075	44
17	383	807	.8585	062	43
18	409	844	.8572	048	42
19	434	882	.8559	034	41
20	.47460	.53920	1.8546	.88020	40
21	486	957	.8533	.88006	39
22	511	.53995	.8520	.87993	38
23	537	.54032	.8507	979	37
24	562	070	.8495	965	36
25	.47588	.54107	1.8482	.87951	35
26	614	145	.8469	937	34
27	639	183	.8456	923	33
28	665	220	.8443	909	32
29	690	258	.8430	896	31
30	.47716	.54296	1.8418	.87882	30
31	741	333	.8405	868	29
32	767	371	.8392	854	28
33	793	409	.8379	840	27
34	818	446	.8367	826	26
35	.47844	.54484	1.8354	.87812	25
36	869	522	.8341	798	24
37	895	560	.8329	784	23
38	920	597	.8316	770	22
39	946	635	.8303	756	21
40	.47971	.54673	1.8291	.87743	20
41	.47997	711	.8278	729	19
42	.48022	748	.8265	715	18
43	048	786	.8253	701	17
44	073	824	.8240	687	16
45	.48099	.54862	1.8228	.87673	15
46	124	900	.8215	659	14
47	150	938	.8202	645	13
48	175	.54975	.8190	631	12
49	201	.55013	.8177	617	11
50	.48226	.55051	1.8165	.87603	10
51	252	089	.8152	589	9
52	277	127	.8140	575	8
53	303	165	.8127	561	7
54	328	203	.8115	546	6
55	.48354	.55241	1.8103	.87532	5
56	379	279	.8090	518	4
57	405	317	.8078	504	3
58	430	355	.8065	490	2
59	456	393	.8053	476	1
60	.48481	.55431	1.8040	.87462	0

| | cos | cot | tan | sin | ′ |

61°

29°

′	sin	tan	cot	cos	
0	.48481	.55431	1.8040	.87462	60
1	506	469	.8028	448	59
2	532	507	.8016	434	58
3	557	545	.8003	420	57
4	583	583	.7991	406	56
5	.48608	.55621	1.7979	.87391	55
6	634	659	.7966	377	54
7	659	697	.7954	363	53
8	684	736	.7942	349	52
9	710	774	.7930	335	51
10	.48735	.55812	1.7917	.87321	50
11	761	850	.7905	306	49
12	786	888	.7893	292	48
13	811	926	.7881	278	47
14	837	.55964	.7868	264	46
15	.48862	.56003	1.7856	.87250	45
16	888	041	.7844	235	44
17	913	079	.7832	221	43
18	938	117	.7820	207	42
19	964	156	.7808	193	41
20	.48989	.56194	1.7796	.87178	40
21	.49014	232	.7783	164	39
22	040	270	.7771	150	38
23	065	309	.7759	136	37
24	090	347	.7747	121	36
25	.49116	.56385	1.7735	.87107	35
26	141	424	.7723	093	34
27	166	462	.7711	079	33
28	192	501	.7699	064	32
29	217	539	.7687	050	31
30	.49242	.56577	1.7675	.87036	30
31	268	616	.7663	021	29
32	293	654	.7651	.87007	28
33	318	693	.7639	.86993	27
34	344	731	.7627	978	26
35	.49369	.56769	1.7615	.86964	25
36	394	808	.7603	949	24
37	419	846	.7591	935	23
38	445	885	.7579	921	22
39	470	923	.7567	906	21
40	.49495	.56962	1.7556	.86892	20
41	521	.57000	.7544	878	19
42	546	039	.7532	863	18
43	571	078·	.7520	849	17
44	596	116	.7508	834	16
45	.49622	.57155	1.7496	.86820	15
46	647	193	.7485	805	14
47	672	232	.7473	791	13
48	697	271	.7461	777	12
49	723	309	.7449	762	11
50	.49748	.57348	1.7437	.86748	10
51	773	386	.7426	733	9
52	798	425	.7414	719	8
53	824	464	.7402	704	7
54	849	503	.7391	690	6
55	.49874	.57541	1.7379	.86675	5
56	899	580	.7367	661	4
57	924	619	.7355	646	3
58	950	657	.7344	632	2
59	.49975	696	.7332	617	1
60	.50000	.57735	1.7321	.86603	0

| | cos | cot | tan | sin | ′ |

60°

′	sin	tan	cot	cos	′
0	.50000	.57735	1.7321	.86603	60
1	025	774	.7309	588	59
2	050	813	.7297	573	58
3	076	851	.7286	559	57
4	101	890	.7274	544	56
5	.50126	.57929	1.7262	.86530	55
6	151	.57968	.7251	515	54
7	176	.58007	.7239	501	53
8	201	046	.7228	486	52
9	227	085	.7216	471	51
10	.50252	.58124	1.7205	.86457	50
11	277	162	.7193	442	49
12	302	201	.7182	427	48
13	327	240	.7170	413	47
14	352	279	.7159	398	46
15	.50377	.58318	1.7147	.86384	45
16	403	357	.7136	369	44
17	428	396	.7124	354	43
18	453	435	.7113	340	42
19	478	474	.7102	325	41
20	.50503	.58513	1.7090	.86310	40
21	528	552	.7079	295	39
22	553	591	.7067	281	38
23	578	631	.7056	266	37
24	603	670	.7045	251	36
25	.50628	.58709	1.7033	.86237	35
26	654	748	.7022	222	34
27	679	787	.7011	207	33
28	704	826	.6999	192	32
29	729	865	.6988	178	31
30	.50754	.58905	1.6977	.86163	30
31	779	944	.6965	148	29
32	804	.58983	.6954	133	28
33	829	.59022	.6943	119	27
34	854	061	.6932	104	26
35	.50879	.59101	1.6920	.86089	25
36	904	140	.6909	074	24
37	929	179	.6898	059	23
38	954	218	.6887	045	22
39	.50979	258	.6875	030	21
40	.51004	.59297	1.6864	.86015	20
41	029	336	.6853	.86000	19
42	054	376	.6842	.85985	18
43	079	415	.6831	970	17
44	104	454	.6820	956	16
45	.51129	.59494	1.6808	.85941	15
46	154	533	.6797	926	14
47	179	573	.6786	911	13
48	204	612	.6775	896	12
49	229	651	.6764	881	11
50	.51254	.59691	1.6753	.85866	10
51	279	730	.6742	851	9
52	304	770	.6731	836	8
53	329	809	.6720	821	7
54	354	849	.6709	806	6
55	.51379	.59888	1.6698	.85792	5
56	404	928	.6687	777	4
57	429	967	.6676	762	3
58	454	.60007	.6665	747	2
59	479	046	.6654	732	1
60	.51504	.60086	1.6643	.85717	0
′	cos	cot	tan	sin	

′	sin	tan	cot	cos	′
0	.51504	.60086	1.6643	.85717	60
1	529	126	.6632	702	59
2	554	165	.6621	687	58
3	579	205	.6610	672	57
4	604	245	.6599	657	56
5	.51628	.60284	1.6588	.85642	55
6	653	324	.6577	627	54
7	678	364	.6566	612	53
8	703	403	.6555	597	52
9	728	443	.6545	582	51
10	.51753	.60483	1.6534	.85567	50
11	778	522	.6523	551	49
12	803	562	.6512	536	48
13	828	602	.6501	521	47
14	852	642	.6490	506	46
15	.51877	.60681	1.6479	.85491	45
16	902	721	.6469	476	44
17	927	761	.6458	461	43
18	952	801	.6447	446	42
19	.51977	841	.6436	431	41
20	.52002	.60881	1.6426	.85416	40
21	026	921	.6415	401	39
22	051	.60960	.6404	385	38
23	076	.61000	.6393	370	37
24	101	040	.6383	355	36
25	.52126	.61080	1.6372	.85340	35
26	151	120	.6361	325	34
27	175	160	.6351	310	33
28	200	200	.6340	294	32
29	225	240	.6329	279	31
30	.52250	.61280	1.6319	.85264	30
31	275	320	.6308	249	29
32	299	360	.6297	234	28
33	324	400	.6287	218	27
34	349	440	.6276	203	26
35	.52374	.61480	1.6265	.85188	25
36	399	520	.6255	173	24
37	423	561	.6244	157	23
38	448	601	.6234	142	22
39	473	641	.6223	127	21
40	.52498	.61681	1.6212	.85112	20
41	522	721	.6202	096	19
42	547	761	.6191	081	18
43	572	801	.6181	066	17
44	597	842	.6170	051	16
45	.52621	.61882	1.6160	.85035	15
46	646	922	.6149	020	14
47	671	.61962	.6139	.85005	13
48	696	.62003	.6128	.84989	12
49	720	043	.6118	974	11
50	.52745	.62083	1.6107	.84959	10
51	770	124	.6097	943	9
52	794	164	.6087	928	8
53	819	204	.6076	913	7
54	844	245	.6066	897	6
55	.52869	.62285	1.6055	.84882	5
56	893	325	.6045	866	4
57	918	366	.6034	851	3
58	943	406	.6024	836	2
59	967	446	.6014	820	1
60	.52992	.62487	1.6003	.84803	0
′	cos	cot	tan	sin	

'	sin	tan	cot	cos	
0	.52992	.62487	1.6003	.84805	60
1	.53017	527	.5993	789	59
2	041	568	.5983	774	58
3	066	608	.5972	759	57
4	091	649	.5962	743	56
5	.53115	.62689	1.5952	.84728	55
6	140	730	.5941	712	54
7	164	770	.5931	697	53
8	189	811	.5921	681	52
9	214	852	.5911	666	51
10	.53238	.62892	1.5900	.84650	50
11	263	933	.5890	635	49
12	288	.62973	.5880	619	48
13	312	.63014	.5869	604	47
14	337	055	.5859	588	46
15	.53361	.63095	1.5849	.84573	45
16	386	136	.5839	557	44
17	411	177	.5829	542	43
18	435	217	.5818	526	42
19	460	258	.5808	511	41
20	.53484	.63299	1.5798	.84495	40
21	509	340	.5788	480	39
22	534	380	.5778	464	38
23	558	421	.5768	448	37
24	583	462	.5757	433	36
25	.53607	.63503	1.5747	.84417	35
26	632	544	.5737	402	34
27	656	584	.5727	386	33
28	681	625	.5717	370	32
29	705	666	.5707	355	31
30	.53730	.63707	1.5697	.84339	30
31	754	748	.5687	324	29
32	779	789	.5677	308	28
33	804	830	.5667	292	27
34	828	871	.5657	277	26
35	.53853	.63912	1.5647	.84261	25
36	877	953	.5637	245	24
37	902	.63994	.5627	230	23
38	926	.64035	.5617	214	22
39	951	076	.5607	198	21
40	.53975	.64117	1.5597	.84182	20
41	.54000	158	.5587	167	19
42	024	199	.5577	151	18
43	049	240	.5567	135	17
44	073	281	.5557	120	16
45	.54097	.64322	1.5547	.84104	15
46	122	363	.5537	088	14
47	146	404	.5527	072	13
48	171	446	.5517	057	12
49	195	487	.5507	041	11
50	.54220	.64528	1.5497	.84025	10
51	244	569	.5487	.84009	9
52	269	610	.5477	.83994	8
53	293	652	.5468	978	7
54	317	693	.5458	962	6
55	.54342	.64734	1.5448	.83946	5
56	366	775	.5438	930	4
57	391	817	.5428	915	3
58	415	858	.5418	899	2
59	440	899	.5408	883	1
60	.54464	.64941	1.5399	.83867	0
	cos	cot	tan	sin	'

'	sin	tan	cot	cos	
0	.54464	.64941	1.5399	.83867	60
1	488	.64982	.5389	851	59
2	513	.65024	.5379	835	58
3	537	065	.5369	819	57
4	561	106	.5359	804	56
5	.54586	.65148	1.5350	.83788	55
6	610	189	.5340	772	54
7	635	231	.5330	756	53
8	659	272	.5320	740	52
9	683	314	.5311	724	51
10	.54708	.65355	1.5301	.83708	50
11	732	397	.5291	692	49
12	756	438	.5282	676	48
13	781	480	.5272	660	47
14	805	521	.5262	645	46
15	.54829	.65563	1.5253	.83629	45
16	854	604	.5243	613	44
17	878	646	.5233	597	43
18	902	688	.5224	581	42
19	927	729	.5214	565	41
20	.54951	.65771	1.5204	.83549	40
21	975	813	.5195	533	39
22	.54999	854	.5185	517	38
23	.55024	896	.5175	501	37
24	048	938	.5166	485	36
25	.55072	.65980	1.5156	.83469	35
26	097	.66021	.5147	453	34
27	121	063	.5137	437	33
28	145	105	.5127	421	32
29	169	147	.5118	405	31
30	.55194	.66189	1.5108	.83389	30
31	218	230	.5099	373	29
32	242	272	.5089	356	28
33	266	314	.5080	340	27
34	291	356	.5070	324	26
35	.55315	.66398	1.5061	.83308	25
36	339	440	.5051	292	24
37	363	482	.5042	276	23
38	388	524	.5032	260	22
39	412	566	.5023	244	21
40	.55436	.66608	1.5013	.83228	20
41	460	650	.5004	212	19
42	484	692	.4994	195	18
43	509	734	.4985	179	17
44	533	776	.4975	163	16
45	.55557	.66818	1.4966	.83147	15
46	581	860	.4957	131	14
47	605	902	.4947	115	13
48	630	944	.4938	098	12
49	654	.66986	.4928	082	11
50	.55678	.67028	1.4919	.83066	10
51	702	071	.4910	050	9
52	726	113	.4900	034	8
53	750	155	.4891	017	7
54	775	197	.4882	.83001	6
55	.55799	.67239	1.4872	.82985	5
56	823	282	.4863	969	4
57	847	324	.4854	953	3
58	871	366	.4844	936	2
59	895	409	.4835	920	1
60	.55919	.67451	1.4826	.82904	0
	cos	cot	tan	sin	'

′	sin	tan	cot	cos	
0	.55919	.67451	1.4826	.82904	60
1	943	493	.4816	887	59
2	968	536	.4807	871	58
3	.55992	578	.4798	855	57
4	.56016	620	.4788	839	56
5	.56040	.67663	1.4779	.82822	55
6	064	705	.4770	806	54
7	088	748	.4761	790	53
8	112	790	.4751	773	52
9	136	832	.4742	757	51
10	.56160	.67875	1.4733	.82741	50
11	184	917	.4724	724	49
12	208	.67960	.4715	708	48
13	232	.68002	.4705	692	47
14	256	045	.4696	675	46
15	.56280	.68088	1.4687	.82659	45
16	305	130	.4678	643	44
17	329	173	.4669	626	43
18	353	215	.4659	610	42
19	377	258	.4650	593	41
20	.56401	.68301	1.4641	.82577	40
21	425	343	.4632	561	39
22	449	386	.4623	544	38
23	473	429	.4614	528	37
24	497	471	.4605	511	36
25	.56521	.68514	1.4596	.82495	35
26	545	557	.4586	478	34
27	569	600	.4577	462	33
28	593	642	.4568	446	32
29	617	685	.4559	429	31
30	.56641	.68728	1.4550	.82413	30
31	665	771	.4541	396	29
32	689	814	.4532	380	28
33	713	857	.4523	363	27
34	736	900	.4514	347	26
35	.56760	.68942	1.4505	.82330	25
36	784	.68985	.4496	314	24
37	808	.69028	.4487	297	23
38	832	071	.4478	281	22
39	856	114	.4469	264	21
40	.56880	.69157	1.4460	.82248	20
41	904	200	.4451	231	19
42	928	243	.4442	214	18
43	952	286	.4433	198	17
44	.56976	329	.4424	181	16
45	.57000	.69372	1.4415	.82165	15
46	024	416	.4406	148	14
47	047	459	.4397	132	13
48	071	502	.4388	115	12
49	095	545	.4379	098	11
50	.57119	.69588	1.4370	.82082	10
51	143	631	.4361	065	9
52	167	675	.4352	048	8
53	191	718	.4344	032	7
54	215	761	.4335	.82015	6
55	.57238	.69804	1.4326	.81999	5
56	262	847	.4317	982	4
57	286	891	.4308	965	3
58	310	934	.4299	949	2
59	334	.69977	.4290	932	1
60	.57358	.70021	1.4281	.81915	0
	cos	cot	tan	sin	′

′	sin	tan	cot	cos	
0	.57358	.70021	1.4281	.81915	60
1	381	064	.4273	899	59
2	405	107	.4264	882	58
3	429	151	.4255	865	57
4	453	194	.4246	848	56
5	.57477	.70238	1.4237	.81832	55
6	501	281	.4229	815	54
7	524	325	.4220	798	53
8	548	368	.4211	782	52
9	572	412	.4202	765	51
10	.57596	.70455	1.4193	.81748	50
11	619	499	.4185	731	49
12	643	542	.4176	714	48
13	667	586	.4167	698	47
14	691	629	.4158	681	46
15	.57715	.70673	1.4150	.81664	45
16	738	717	.4141	647	44
17	762	760	.4132	631	43
18	786	804	.4124	614	42
19	810	848	.4115	597	41
20	.57833	.70891	1.4106	.81580	40
21	857	935	.4097	563	39
22	881	.70979	.4089	546	38
23	904	.71023	.4080	530	37
24	928	066	.4071	513	36
25	.57952	.71110	1.4063	.81496	35
26	976	154	.4054	479	34
27	.57999	198	.4045	462	33
28	.58023	242	.4037	445	32
29	047	285	.4028	428	31
30	.58070	.71329	1.4019	.81412	30
31	094	373	.4011	395	29
32	118	417	.4002	378	28
33	141	461	.3994	361	27
34	165	505	.3985	344	26
35	.58189	.71549	1.3976	.81327	25
36	212	593	.3968	310	24
37	236	637	.3959	293	23
38	260	681	.3951	276	22
39	283	725	.3942	259	21
40	.58307	.71769	1.3934	.81242	20
41	330	813	.3925	225	19
42	354	857	.3916	208	18
43	378	901	.3908	191	17
44	401	946	.3899	174	16
45	.58425	.71990	1.3891	.81157	15
46	449	.72034	.3882	140	14
47	472	078	.3874	123	13
48	496	122	.3865	106	12
49	519	167	.3857	089	11
50	.58543	.72211	1.3848	.81072	10
51	567	255	.3840	055	9
52	590	299	.3831	038	8
53	614	344	.3823	021	7
54	637	388	.3814	.81004	6
55	.58661	.72432	1.3806	80987	5
56	684	477	.3798	970	4
57	708	521	.3789	953	3
58	731	565	.3781	936	2
59	755	610	.3772	919	1
60	.58779	.72654	1.3764	.80902	0
	cos	cot	tan	sin	′

′	sin	tan	cot	cos	
0	.58779	.72654	1.3764	.80902	60
1	802	699	.3755	885	59
2	826	743	.3747	867	58
3	849	788	.3739	850	57
4	873	832	.3730	833	56
5	.58896	.72877	1.3722	.80816	55
6	920	921	.3713	799	54
7	943	.72966	.3705	782	53
8	967	.73010	.3697	765	52
9	58990	055	.3688	748	51
10	.59014	.73100	1.3680	.80730	50
11	037	144	.3672	713	49
12	061	189	.3663	696	48
13	084	234	.3655	679	47
14	108	278	.3647	662	46
15	.59131	.73323	1.3638	.80644	45
16	154	368	.3630	627	44
17	178	413	.3622	610	43
18	201	457	.3613	593	42
19	225	502	.3605	576	41
20	.59248	.73547	1.3597	.80558	40
21	272	592	.3588	541	39
22	295	637	.3580	524	38
23	318	681	.3572	507	37
24	342	726	.3564	489	36
25	.59365	.73771	1.3555	.80472	35
26	389	816	.3547	455	34
27	412	861	.3539	438	33
28	436	906	.3531	420	32
29	459	951	.3522	403	31
30	.59482	.73996	1.3514	.80386	30
31	506	74041	.3506	368	29
32	529	086	.3498	351	28
33	552	131	.3490	334	27
34	576	176	.3481	316	26
35	.59599	.74221	1.3473	.80299	25
36	622	267	.3465	282	24
37	646	312	.3457	264	23
38	669	357	.3449	247	22
39	693	402	.3440	230	21
40	.59716	.74447	1.3432	.80212	20
41	739	492	.3424	195	19
42	763	538	.3416	178	18
43	786	583	.3408	160	17
44	809	628	.3400	143	16
45	.59832	.74674	1.3392	.80125	15
46	856	719	.3384	108	14
47	879	764	.3375	091	13
48	902	810	.3367	073	12
49	926	855	.3359	056	11
50	59949	.74900	1.3351	.80038	10
51	972	946	.3343	021	9
52	59995	.74991	.3335	.80003	8
53	.60019	.75037	.3327	.79986	7
54	042	082	.3319	968	6
55	.60065	.75128	1.3311	.79951	5
56	089	173	.3303	934	4
57	112	219	.3295	916	3
58	135	264	.3287	899	2
59	158	310	.3278	881	1
60	.60182	.75355	1.3270	.79864	0
	cos	cot	tan	sin	′

′	sin	tan	cot	cos	
0	.60182	.75355	1.3270	.79864	60
1	205	401	.3262	846	59
2	228	447	.3254	829	58
3	251	492	.3246	811	57
4	274	538	.3238	793	56
5	.60298	.75584	1.3230	.79776	55
6	321	629	.3222	758	54
7	344	675	.3214	741	53
8	367	721	.3206	723	52
9	390	767	.3198	706	51
10	.60414	.75812	1.3190	.79688	50
11	437	858	.3182	671	49
12	460	904	.3175	653	48
13	483	950	.3167	635	47
14	506	.75996	.3159	618	46
15	.60529	.76042	1.3151	.79600	45
16	553	088	.3143	583	44
17	576	134	.3135	565	43
18	599	180	.3127	547	42
19	622	226	.3119	530	41
20	.60645	.76272	1.3111	.79512	40
21	668	318	.3103	494	39
22	691	364	.3095	477	38
23	714	410	.3087	459	37
24	738	456	.3079	441	36
25	.60761	.76502	1.3072	.79424	35
26	784	548	.3064	406	34
27	807	594	.3056	388	33
28	830	640	.3048	371	32
29	853	686	.3040	353	31
30	.60876	.76733	1.3032	.79335	30
31	899	779	.3024	318	29
32	922	825	.3017	300	28
33	945	871	.3009	282	27
34	968	918	.3001	264	26
35	.60991	.76964	1.2993	.79247	25
36	.61015	.77010	.2985	229	24
37	038	057	.2977	211	23
38	061	103	.2970	193	22
39	084	149	.2962	176	21
40	.61107	.77196	1.2954	.79158	20
41	130	242	.2946	140	19
42	153	289	.2938	122	18
43	176	335	.2931	105	17
44	199	382	.2923	087	16
45	.61222	.77428	1.2915	.79069	15
46	245	475	.2907	051	14
47	268	521	.2900	033	13
48	291	568	.2892	.79016	12
49	314	615	.2884	.78998	11
50	.61337	.77661	1.2876	.78980	10
51	360	708	.2869	962	9
52	383	754	.2861	944	8
53	406	801	.2853	926	7
54	429	848	.2846	908	6
55	.61451	.77895	1.2838	.78891	5
56	474	941	.2830	873	4
57	497	.77988	.2822	855	3
58	520	.78035	.2815	837	2
59	543	082	.2807	819	1
60	.61566	.78129	1.2799	.78801	0
	cos	cot	tan	sin	′

′	sin	tan	cot	cos	
0	.61566	.78129	1.2799	.78801	60
1	589	175	.2792	783	59
2	612	222	.2784	765	58
3	635	269	.2776	747	57
4	658	316	.2769	729	56
5	.61681	.78363	1.2761	.78711	55
6	704	410	.2753	694	54
7	726	457	.2746	676	53
8	749	504	.2738	658	52
9	772	551	.2731	640	51
10	.61795	.78598	1.2723	.78622	50
11	818	645	.2715	604	49
12	841	692	.2708	586	48
13	864	739	.2700	568	47
14	887	786	.2693	550	46
15	.61909	.78834	1.2685	.78532	45
16	932	881	.2677	514	44
17	955	928	.2670	496	43
18	.61978	.78975	.2662	478	42
19	.62001	.79022	.2655	460	41
20	.62024	.79070	1.2647	.78442	40
21	046	117	.2640	424	39
22	069	164	.2632	405	38
23	092	212	.2624	387	37
24	115	259	.2617	369	36
25	.62138	.79306	1.2609	.78351	35
26	160	354	.2602	333	34
27	183	401	.2594	315	33
28	206	449	.2587	297	32
29	229	496	.2579	279	31
30	.62251	.79544	1.2572	.78261	30
31	274	591	.2564	243	29
32	297	639	.2557	225	28
33	320	686	.2549	206	27
34	342	734	.2542	188	26
35′	.62365	.79781	1.2534	.78170	25
36	388	829	.2527	152	24
37	411	877	.2519	134	23
38	433	924	.2512	116	22
39	456	.79972	.2504	098	21
40	.62479	.80020	1.2497	.78079	20
41	502	067	.2489	061	19
42	524	115	.2482	043	18
43	547	163	.2475	025	17
44	570	211	.2467	.78007	16
45	.62592	.80258	1.2460	.77988	15
46	615	306	.2452	970	14
47	638	354	.2445	952	13
48	660	402	.2437	934	12
49	683	450	.2430	916	11
50	.62706	.80498	1.2423	.77897	10
51	728	546	.2415	879	9
52	751	594	.2408	861	8
53	774	642	.2401	843	7
54	796	690	.2393	824	6
55	.62819	.80738	1.2386	.77806	5
56	842	786	.2378	788	4
57	864	834	.2371	769	3
58	887	882	.2364	751	2
59	909	930	.2356	733	1
60	.62932	.80978	1.2349	.77715	0
	cos	cot	tan	sin	′

′	sin	tan	cot	cos	
0	.62932	.80978	1.2349	.77715	60
1	955	.81027	.2342	696	59
2	.62977	075	.2334	678	58
3	.63000	123	.2327	660	57
4	022	171	.2320	641	56
5	.63045	.81220	1.2312	.77623	55
6	068	268	.2305	605	54
7	090	316	.2298	586	53
8	113	364	.2290	568	52
9	135	413	.2283	550	51
10	.63158	.81461	1.2276	.77531	50
11	180	510	.2268	513	49
12	203	558	.2261	494	48
13	225	606	.2254	476	47
14	248	655	.2247	458	46
15	.63271	.81703	1.2239	.77439	45
16	293	752	.2232	421	44
17	316	800	.2225	402	43
18	338	849	.2218	384	42
19	361	898	.2210	366	41
20	.63383	.81946	1.2203	.77347	40
21	406	.81995	.2196	329	39
22	428	.82044	.2189	310	38
23	451	092	.2181	292	37
24	473	141	.2174	273	36
25	.63496	.82190	1.2167	.77255	35
26	518	238	.2160	236	34
27	540	287	.2153	218	33
28	563	336	.2145	199	32
29	585	385	.2138	181	31
30	.63608	.82434	1.2131	.77162	30
31	630	483	.2124	144	29
32	653	531	.2117	125	28
33	675	580	.2109	107	27
34	698	629	.2102	088	26
35	.63720	.82678	1.2095	.77070	25
36	742	727	.2088	051	24
37	765	776	.2081	033	23
38	787	825	.2074	.77014	22
39	810	874	.2066	.76996	21
40	.63832	.82923	1.2059	.76977	20
41	854	.82972	.2052	959	19
42	877	.83022	.2045	940	18
43	899	071	.2038	921	17
44	922	120	.2031	903	16
45	.63944	.83169	1.2024	.76884	15
46	966	218	.2017	866	14
47	.63989	268	.2009	847	13
48	.64011	317	.2002	828	12
49	033	366	.1995	810	11
50	.64056	.83415	1.1988	.76791	10
51	078	465	.1981	772	9
52	100	514	.1974	754	8
53	123	564	.1967	735	7
54	145	613	.1960	717	6
55	.64167	.83662	1.1953	.76698	5
56	190	712	.1946	679	4
57	212	761	.1939	661	3
58	234	811	.1932	642	2
59	256	860	.1925	623	1
60	.64279	.83910	1.1918	.76604	0
	cos	cot	tan	sin	′

40°

′	sin	tan	cot	cos	
0	.64279	.83910	1.1918	.76604	60
1	301	83960	.1910	586	59
2	323	.84009	.1903	567	58
3	346	059	.1896	548	57
4	368	108	.1889	530	56
5	.64390	.84158	1.1882	.76511	55
6	412	208	.1875	492	54
7	435̄	258	.1868	473	53
8	457	307	.1861	455	52
9	479	357	.1854	436	51
10	.64501	.84407	1.1847	.76417	50
11	524	457	.1840	398	49
12	546	507	.1833	380	48
13	568	556	.1826	361	47
14	590	606	.1819	342	46
15	.64612	.84656	1.1812	.76323	45
16	635̄	706	.1806	304	44
17	657	756	.1799	286	43
18	679	806	.1792	267	42
19	701	856	.1785	248	41
20	.64723	.84906	1.1778	.76229	40
21	746	.84956	1771	210	39
22	768	.85006	.1764	192	38
23	790	057	.1757	173	37
24	812	107	.1750	154	36
25	.64834	.85157	1.1743	.76135	35
26	856	207	.1736	116	34
27	878	257	.1729	097	33
28	901	308	.1722	078	32
29	923	358	.1715	059	31
30	.64945̄	.85408	1.1708	.76041	30
31	967	458	.1702	022	29
32	64989	509	.1695	.76003	28
33	.65011	559	.1688	.75984	27
34	033	609	.1681	965	26
35	.65055	.85660	1.1674	.75946	25
36	077	710	.1667	927	24
37	100	761	.1660	908	23
38	122	811	.1653	889	22
39	144	862	.1647	870	21
40	.65166	.85912	1.1640	.75851	20
41	188	.85963	.1633	832	19
42	210	.86014	.1626	813	18
43	232	064	.1619	794	17
44	254	115̄	.1612	775	16
45	.65276	.86166	1.1606	.75756	15
46	298	216	.1599	738	14
47	320	267	.1592	719	13
48	342	318	.1585	700	12
49	364	368	.1578	680	11
50	.65386	.86419	1.1571	.75661	10
51	408	470	.1565̄	642	9
52	430	521	.1558	623	8
53	452	572	.1551	604	7
54	474	623	.1544	585	6
55	.65496	.86674	1.1538	.75566	5
56	518	725̄	.1531	547	4
57	540	776	.1524	528	3
58	562	827	.1517	509	2
59	584	878	.1510	490	1
60	.65606	.86929	1.1504	.75471	0
	cos	cot	tan	sin	′

49°

41°

′	sin	tan	cot	cos	
0	.65606	.86929	1.1504	.75471	60
1	628	.86980	.1497	452	59
2	650	.87031	.1490	433	58
3	672	082	.1483	414	57
4	694	133	.1477	395	56
5	.65716	.87184	1.1470	.75375	55
6	738	236	.1463	356	54
7	759	287	.1456	337	53
8	781	338	.1450̄	318	52
9	803	389	.1443	299	51
10	.65825	.87441	1.1436	.75280	50
11	847	492	.1430	261	49
12	869	543	.1423	241	48
13	891	595	.1416	222	47
14	913	646	.1410	203	46
15	.65935̄	.87698	1.1403	.75184	45
16	956	749	.1396	165	44
17	.65978	801	.1389	146	43
18	.66000	852	.1383	126	42
19	022	904	.1376	107	41
20	.66044	.87955	1.1369	.75088	40
21	066	.88007	.1363	069	39
22	088	059	.1356	050	38
23	109	110	.1349	030	37
24	131	162	.1343	.75011	36
25	.66153	.88214	1.1336	.74992	35
26	175	265	.1329	973	34
27	197	317	.1323	953	33
28	218	369	.1316	934	32
29	240	421	.1310	915	31
30	.66262	.88473	1.1303	.74896	30
31	284	524	.1296	876	29
32	306	576	.1290	857	28
33	327	628	.1283	838	27
34	349	680	.1276	818	26
35	.66371	.88732	1.1270	.74799	25
36	393	784	.1263	780	24
37	414	836	.1257	760	23
38	436	888	.1250	741	22
39	458	940	.1243	722	21
40	.66480	.88992	1.1237	.74703	20
41	501	.89045̄	.1230	683	19
42	523	097	.1224	664	18
43	545	149	.1217	644	17
44	566	201	.1211	625	16
45	.66588	.89253	1.1204	.74606	15
46	610	306	.1197	586	14
47	632	358	.1191	567	13
48	653	410	.1184	548	12
49	675̄	463	.1178	528	11
50	.66697	.89515	1.1171	.74509	10
51	718	567	.1165̄	489	9
52	740	620	.1158	470	8
53	762	672	.1152	451	7
54	783	725̄	.1145	431	6
55	.66805̄	.89777	1.1139	.74412	5
56	827	830	.1132	392	4
57	848	883	.1126	373	3
58	870	935	.1119	353	2
59	891	.89988	.1113	334	1
60	.66913	.90040	1.1106	.74314	0
	cos	cot	tan	sin	′

48°

110

42°

'	sin	tan	cot	cos	
0	.66913	.90040	1.1106	.74314	60
1	935	093	.1100	295	59
2	956	146	.1093	276	58
3	978	199	.1087	256	57
4	.66999	251	.1080	237	56
5	.67021	.90304	1.1074	.74217	55
6	043	357	.1067	198	54
7	064	410	.1061	178	53
8	086	463	.1054	159	52
9	107	516	.1048	139	51
10	.67129	.90569	1.1041	.74120	50
11	151	621	.1035	100	49
12	172	674	.1028	080	48
13	194	727	.1022	061	47
14	215	781	.1016	041	46
15	.67237	.90834	1.1009	.74022	45
16	258	887	.1003	74002	44
17	280	940	.0996	.73983	43
18	301	.90993	.0990	963	42
19	323	.91046	.0983	944	41
20	.67344	.91099	1.0977	.73924	40
21	366	153	.0971	904	39
22	387	206	.0964	885	38
23	409	259	.0958	865	37
24	430	313	.0951	846	36
25	.67452	.91366	1.0945	.73826	35
26	473	419	.0939	806	34
27	495	473	.0932	787	33
28	516	526	.0926	767	32
29	538	580	.0919	747	31
30	.67559	.91633	1.0913	.73728	30
31	580	687	.0907	708	29
32	602	740	.0900	688	28
33	623	794	.0894	669	27
34	645	847	.0888	649	26
35	.67666	.91901	1.0881	.73629	25
36	688	.91955	.0875	610	24
37	709	.92008	.0869	590	23
38	730	062	.0862	570	22
39	752	116	.0856	551	21
40	.67773	.92170	1.0850	.73531	20
41	795	224	.0843	511	19
42	816	277	.0837	491	18
43	837	331	.0831	472	17
44	859	385	.0824	452	16
45	.67880	.92439	1.0818	.73432	15
46	901	493	.0812	413	14
47	923	547	.0805	393	13
48	944	601	.0799	373	12
49	965	655	.0793	353	11
50	.67987	.92709	1.0786	.73333	10
51	.68008	763	.0780	314	9
52	029	817	.0774	294	8
53	051	872	.0768	274	7
54	072	926	.0761	254	6
55	.68093	.92980	1.0755	.73234	5
56	115	.93034	.0749	215	4
57	136	088	.0742	195	3
58	157	143	.0736	175	2
59	179	197	.0730	155	1
60	.68200	.93252	1.0724	.73135	0
	cos	cot	tan	sin	'

47°

43°

'	sin	tan	cot	cos	
0	.68200	.93252	1.0724	.73135	60
1	221	306	.0717	116	59
2	242	360	.0711	096	58
3	264	415	.0705	076	57
4	285	469	.0699	056	56
5	.68306	.93524	1.0692	.73036	55
6	327	578	.0686	.73016	54
7	349	633	.0680	.72996	53
8	370	688	.0674	976	52
9	391	742	.0668	957	51
10	.68412	.93797	1.0661	.72937	50
11	434	852	.0655	917	49
12	455	906	.0649	897	48
13	476	.93961	.0643	877	47
14	497	.94016	.0637	857	46
15	.68518	.94071	1.0630	.72837	45
16	539	125	.0624	817	44
17	561	180	.0618	797	43
18	582	235	.0612	777	42
19	603	290	.0606	757	41
20	.68624	.94345	1.0599	.72737	40
21	645	400	.0593	717	39
22	666	455	.0587	697	38
23	688	510	.0581	677	37
24	709	565	.0575	657	36
25	.68730	.94620	1.0569	.72637	35
26	751	676	.0562	617	34
27	772	731	.0556	597	33
28	793	786	.0550	577	32
29	814	841	.0544	557	31
30	.68835	.94896	1.0538	.72537	30
31	857	.94952	.0532	517	29
32	878	.95007	.0526	497	28
33	899	062	.0519	477	27
34	920	118	.0513	457	26
35	.68941	.95173	1.0507	.72437	25
36	962	229	.0501	417	24
37	.68983	284	.0495	397	23
38	.69004	340	.0489	377	22
39	025	395	.0483	357	21
40	.69046	.95451	1.0477	.72337	20
41	067	506	.0470	317	19
42	088	562	.0464	297	18
43	109	618	.0458	277	17
44	130	673	.0452	257	16
45	.69151	.95729	1.0446	.72236	15
46	172	785	.0440	216	14
47	193	841	.0434	196	13
48	214	897	.0428	176	12
49	235	.95952	.0422	156	11
50	.69256	.96008	1.0416	.72136	10
51	277	064	.0410	116	9
52	298	120	.0404	095	8
53	319	176	.0398	075	7
54	340	232	.0392	055	6
55	.69361	.96288	1.0385	.72035	5
56	382	344	.0379	.72015	4
57	403	400	.0373	.71995	3
58	424	457	.0367	974	2
59	445	513	.0361	954	1
60	.69466	.96569	1.0355	.71934	0
	cos	cot	tan	sin	'

46°

′	sin	tan	cot	cos	
0	.69466	.96569	1.0355	.71934	60
1	487	625	.0349	914	59
2	508	681	.0343	894	58
3	529	738	.0337	873	57
4	549	794	.0331	853	56
5	.69570	.96850	1.0325	.71833	55
6	591	907	.0319	813	54
7	612	.96963	.0313	792	53
8	633	.97020	.0307	772	52
9	654	076	.0301	752	51
10	.69675	.97133	1.0295	.71732	50
11	696	189	.0289	711	49
12	717	246	.0283	691	48
13	737	302	.0277	671	47
14	758	359	.0271	650	46
15	.69779	.97416	1.0265	.71630	45
16	800	472	.0259	610	44
17	821	529	.0253	590	43
18	842	586	.0247	569	42
19	862	643	.0241	549	41
20	.69883	.97700	1.0235	.71529	40
21	904	756	.0230	508	39
22	925	813	.0224	488	38
23	946	870	.0218	468	37
24	966	927	.0212	447	36
25	.69987	.97984	1.0206	.71427	35
26	.70008	.98041	.0200	407	34
27	029	098	.0194	386	33
28	049	155	.0188	366	32
29	070	213	.0182	345	31
30	.70091	.98270	1.0176	.71325	30
31	112	327	.0170	305	29
32	132	384	.0164	284	28
33	153	441	.0158	264	27
34	174	499	.0152	243	26
35	.70195	.98556	1.0147	.71223	25
36	215	613	.0141	203	24
37	236	671	.0135	182	23
38	257	728	.0129	162	22
39	277	786	.0123	141	21
40	.70298	.98843	1.0117	.71121	20
41	319	901	.0111	100	19
42	339	.98958	.0105	080	18
43	360	.99016	.0099	059	17
44	381	073	.0094	039	16
45	.70401	.99131	1.0088	.71019	15
46	422	189	.0082	.70998	14
47	443	247	.0076	978	13
48	463	304	.0070	957	12
49	484	362	.0064	937	11
50	.70505	.99420	1.0058	.70916	10
51	525	478	.0052	896	9
52	546	536	.0047	875	8
53	567	594	.0041	855	7
54	587	652	.0035	834	6
55	.70608	.99710	1.0029	.70813	5
56	628	768	.0023	793	4
57	649	826	.0017	772	3
58	670	884	.0012	752	2
59	690	.99942	.0006	731	1
60	.70711	1.0000	1.0000	.70711	0
	cos	cot	tan	sin	

Catalog

If you are interested in a list of fine Paperback
books, covering a wide range of subjects
and interests, send your name and address,
requesting your free catalog, to:

McGraw-Hill Paperbacks
1221 Avenue of Americas
New York, N.Y. 10020